全国英语等级考试(PETS)规划系列丛书

全国英语等级考试(PETS)全真模拟测试
(第二级)

■ 本书主编　钱　丽

■ 本书副主编　孙　佳　朱晓卿　崔轶婷

■ 本书编者　张　琦　张　妮　陈　斌　杨桂林

■ 丛书编委（以姓氏笔画为序）
王玲霞　王　前　王　影　王琳霞　毛英芝
朱绍昌　许小明　刘向萍　刘红梅　刘　宏
汤定军　杨　健　杨梅青　杨　新　吴　魏
狄　丹　汪　蕊　张建初　张　静　陈　湘
房宝娟　赵　丹　胡晓红　顾　清　耿曙生
龚华刚　蒋秉章　蔡　军　管兆宁　魏荣华
濮海慧

■ 丛书策划　汤定军　管兆宁

苏州大学出版社

前　言

全国英语等级考试(PETS)从开考以来已经有十几年的时间了。随着时间的推移，PETS 在全国的影响力不断扩大，参加考试的人数也逐年递增，现在每年全国参加考试的人数已达数百万，PETS 考试成绩也被社会所接受，成为学历考试和其他考核的有力依据，该项考试成绩的可信度、有效度也越来越被社会所公认。

全国英语等级考试(PETS)是一项社会考试，考生来自企业、事业、行政等单位和在校学生。大部分考生在考前没有完整的时间进行系统学习，他们往往在工作和正常学习之余靠自学来掌握必备的知识和考试技巧，用自己的勤奋和智慧取得考试的成功。因此，他们迫切需要一套知识比较全面、质量比较上乘的 PETS 培训教材和教学辅导用书来帮助他们系统地、有效地复习自己已经学过的英语知识，给予他们必要的、富有成效的指导。通过教材的讲解、辅导和做练习，他们能掌握考试要求的词汇、语法、口语等英语知识和一系列的应试技巧。

为了满足 PETS 考生的需求，为我国教育事业做出贡献，苏州大学出版社组织了全国部分高校的一线专业教师和全国著名的教育培训机构对 PETS 考试大纲进行认真学习和研究，并对 PETS 考生做了一系列的社会调查，进而了解他们需要什么样的教材，在此基础上着手梳理出《全国英语等级考试(PETS)规划丛书编写大纲》，花了大量时间对编写人员进行培训、学习，让他们吃透编写的要点、重点，有针对性地选材、组合和分类。《全国英语等级考试(PETS)规划系列丛书》总主编为全国英语等级考试(PETS)资深专家、上海教育考试院 PETS 专家组组长、上海应用技术学院蒋秉章教授。

《全国英语等级考试(PETS)规划系列丛书》包括《综合教程》、《实战攻略》和《全真模拟测试》。《综合教程》包括课文、课文理解和练习；语法讲解和练习；考试分项练习(听力理解、阅读理解、英语运用和写作)。《实战攻略》辅导用书主要是解题技巧指导、模拟试题及讲解。《全真模拟测试》包括 10 套全真模拟测试卷。《综合教程》、《实战攻略》和《全真模拟测试》提供了所有练习的答案、听力录音、听力材料等，《综合教程》还配备了课件。

该套丛书可供各类学校、培训机构培训时教学使用，也可供自学者自学使用。

该教材在编写和出版过程中得到了苏州大学出版社领导、外籍专家和专职编辑的大力指导和帮助，在此我们深表感谢。

由于编者本身的水平有限，书中错误之处在所难免，请各位同仁和读者不吝赐教，我们表示万分感谢。

编　者

2015 年 12 月

图书在版编目(CIP)数据

全国英语等级考试(PETS)全真模拟测试. 第二级 / 钱丽主编. —苏州：苏州大学出版社，2013.7(2019.9 重印)
(全国英语等级考试(PETS)规划系列丛书)
ISBN 978-7-5672-0560-4

Ⅰ.①全… Ⅱ.①钱… Ⅲ.①全国公共英语等级考试—习题集 Ⅳ.①H319.6

中国版本图书馆 CIP 数据核字(2013)第 166610 号

本书配有听力录音，请使用单位或个人登录 www.sudapress.com，或联系汤定军先生(tangdingjun@suda.edu.cn，0512-65222096)。

书　　名：全国英语等级考试(PETS)全真模拟测试
(第二级)

主　　编：钱　丽
责任编辑：沈　琴
策划编辑：汤定军　管兆宁
封面设计：刘　俊

出版发行：苏州大学出版社(Soochow University Press)
社　　址：苏州市十梓街 1 号　**邮编**：215006
印　　刷：常州市武进第三印刷有限公司
网　　址：www.sudapress.com
E-mail　：tangdingjun@suda.edu.cn
邮购热线：0512-67480030
销售热线：0512-65225020

开　　本：787 mm×1 092 mm　1/8　**印张**：8.75　**字数**：213 千
版　　次：2013 年 7 月第 1 版
印　　次：2019 年 9 月第 4 次印刷
书　　号：ISBN 978-7-5672-0560-4
定　　价：22.00 元

Contents
目 录

全国英语等级考试
第二级
PUBLIC ENGLISH TEST SYSTEM (PETS)
LEVEL 2

全真模拟卷(1)

第一部分　听　力

第一节

听下面5段对话。每段对话后有一个小题,从题中所给的A、B、C三个选项中选出最佳选项,并标在试卷的相应位置。听完每段对话后,你都有10秒钟的时间来回答有关小题和阅读下一小题。每段对话仅读一遍。

例: How much is the shirt? A. £19.15.　　B. £9.15.　　C. £9.18. 答案:C

1. Where does the woman prefer to live?
   A. She prefers to live in big cities.
   B. She prefers to live in another county.
   C. She prefers to live in the country.
2. What does the man mean?
   A. He wants to buy a new glass for the woman.
   B. He will take the broken glasses away.
   C. He asks the woman to get another glass for him.
3. What are the speakers talking about?
   A. A child.　　B. A room.　　C. A present.
4. What can we learn from this conversation?
   A. The woman does not get along well with the man.
   B. The woman does not get along well with her roommate.
   C. The man will talk with the woman's roommate.
5. Where are the two speakers now?
   A. On the first floor.　　B. On the fourth floor.　　C. On the fifth floor.

第二节

听下面几段对话或独白。每段对话或独白后有2至4个小题,从题中所给的A、B、C三

个选项中选出最佳选项,并标在试卷的相应位置。听每段对话或独白前,你将有5秒钟的时间阅读各个小题;听完后,各小题将给出5秒钟的作答时间。每段对话或独白读两遍。

听下面一段对话,回答第6和第7题。

6. What was the woman doing before she went home?

A. Typing a report. B. Rewriting a report. C. Reviewing a report.

7. Where did the woman have her dinner?

A. In a restaurant. B. In her office. C. At home.

听下面一段对话,回答第8和第9题。

8. Why does the man feel surprised?

A. The woman has found a new job.

B. The woman doesn't feel like leaving.

C. The woman disagrees with him.

9. What does the woman say about her department?

A. There is a lack of trust.

B. There are serious problems.

C. There is too much pressure.

听下面一段对话,回答第10至第12题。

10. What are the speakers talking about?

A. Popular sports events.

B. TV programs people like best.

C. Things people do after work.

11. How did the woman do the research?

A. She talked to people.

B. She sent letters to people.

C. She collected information from newspapers.

12. What do most people do in their spare time?

A. Go to movies. B. Read books. C. Watch TV.

听下面一段对话,回答第13至第16题。

13. Where does this conversation take place?

A. At the airport. B. In a restaurant. C. On the street.

14. Why does the woman like San Francisco?

A. It has less traffic.

B. It has the best food and music.

C. People there are friendlier.

15. Where does the woman come from?

A. Pennsylvania. B. San Francisco. C. China.

16. What does the woman think of the man's English?

A. Excellent. B. Acceptable. C. Strange.

听下面一段对话,回答第17至第20题。

17. How many people are there in the woman's family?

A. Three. B. Four. C. Five.

18. What did the children think about having dinner together at home?

A. They thought it was funny.

B. They disliked the idea at first.

C. They preferred eating with friends.

19. How often did the family finally decide to have meals together?

A. Every Sunday. B. Twice a week. C. Three times a week.

20. Who finally set the time for these family dinners?

A. The children. B. The father. C. The woman speaker.

第二部分 阅 读

第一节 短文理解

阅读下列短文，从每题所给的 A、B、C 和 D 四个选项中，选出最佳选项，并在答题卡上将该项涂黑。

Text 1

Cancer is feared by everyone. And this fear is reaching epidemic(流行性) proportions. Not the disease itself—there is no such thing as a cancer epidemic. Except for lung cancer, mostly caused by cigarette smoking, the incidence rates are leveling off, and in the case of some kinds of cancer are decreasing. But the fear of cancer is catching, and the country stands at risk of an anxiety. The earth itself is coming to seem like a huge carcinogen(致癌物). The ordinary, more or less scientific statement that something between 80 and 90 percent of all cancers are due to things in the environment is taken to mean that none of us will be safe until the whole environment is "cleaned up". This is not at all the meaning.

The 80-percent calculation is based on the unthinkable differences in the incidence of cancer in various societies around the world—for example, the high proportion of liver cancer in Africa and the Far East, stomach cancer in Japan, breast cancer in Western Europe and North America, and the relatively low figures for breast cancer in Japan and parts of Africa and for liver cancer in America. These data indicate there may be special and specific environmental influences, largely based on personal life-style, that determine the incidence of various forms of cancer in different communities—but that is all the data suggest. The overall incidence of cancer, counting up all the cases, is probable roughly the same everywhere.

21. Which of the following is the closest in meaning to the phrase "leveling off"?

A. Becoming very popular

B. Reaching its lowest level in popularity

C. Stopping being popular

D. Stopping increasing its popularity

22. According to the passage, the incidence of cancer is generally believed ________.

A. to be based on inactive life style

B. to be due to anxiety

C. to result from environmental influences

D. to be caused by heavy smoking

23. It can be inferred from the passage that the writer's opinion about the relationship between cancer and environment is ________.

A. positive B. negative C. neutral D. approving

Text 2

Tom Smith lived on an island off the east coast of the New Territories. Most of the people on the island were farmers or fishermen. Tom was studying at a school in Kowloon.

A few years ago, there was a severe storm soon after Tom's sixteenth birthday. The fishing boats hurried to a typhoon shelter at Tai Po. The harbor of the island was too small and unsafe in a storm.

During the storm, an old woman named Mrs. Yeung became seriously ill. There was a small boat on the island but the waves smashed it when some men tried to put it on the sea.

Mrs. Yeung's married son tried to swim across to Sai Kung to get help but he nearly drowned in the rough sea. Another man tried to swim across to Sai Kung to get a helicopter or police launch but he failed too.

Finally, Tom Smith asked his parents if he could try. Mrs. Yeung was his great-aunt, so Mr. and Mrs. Smith let Tom try. They tied a rope round his waist and shoulder before he went into the water.

Tom had to struggle very hard to swim through the big waves. He was lucky because the storm kept the sharks away. Finally he reached Sai Kung. He went to a police station and soon a police launch went to the island. Some men carried Mrs. Yeung through the sea to the launch and it took her to hospital.

Two weeks later, Mrs. Yeung was well enough to return to the island. All the people on the island were very proud of Tom because of his bravery.

24. There wasn't a typhoon shelter on the island, was there?

A. Yes, there wasn't. B. No, there was.

C. No, there wasn't. D. Yes, there was.

25. Why did some men try to launch a small boat?

A. To reach the typhoon shelter at Tai Po.

B. To go and get Mrs. Yeung at Sai Kung.

C. To help the lady who was very ill.

D. To catch some fish for the sick lady.

26. In the second paragraph, a severe storm is one which ________.

A. is very hard or powerful

B. lasts for many days

C. comes at the wrong time of the year

D. is often seen

27. To reach Sai Kung, Tom probably had to swim towards the ________.

A. east B. west C. south D. north

Text 3

Welcome to our small business set-up guide, providing all the information you need to start your business on a healthy, solid basis.

From choosing the right name for your company and making your first business plan, through to up-to-date taxation(税务) advice, banking and insurance tips, each subject is discussed in the guide.

We also look at the vital characteristics you'll need to survive in business. Determination and originality(原创性) are key. Equally, so is the ability to organize your time and to put in the required effort during the early days.

As with any new business, success can never be guaranteed, but our aim is to reduce the difficulties involved in setting up a business on your own. We'll forewarn you of the most common problems, including failure to research your market in sufficient detail and not setting aside enough funds for tougher financial times.

Starting up even the smallest business can be challenging. But take comfort in the fact that you are not alone. In fact, of the four million businesses currently in operation in the UK, more than 99.3% are classified as "small", with fewer than 50 employees.

In order to keep this guide as brief as possible, where we've not had enough room to include every detail, you'll find a link taking you to the most relevant(相关的) articles.

Good luck with your business idea!

28. This guide is intended to help people to ________.

A. cope with an economic crisis　　B. start a new small business

C. raise funds for a new firm　　D. build up public relations

29. What are most important for a business to survive?

A. Banking and insurance services.　　B. Research and business planning.

C. Organization and management.　　D. Determination and originality.

30. What does the word "forewarn" (Line 2, Para. 4) mean?

A. Deal with.　　B. Argue with.

C. Advise beforehand.　　D. Give instructions to.

第二节　补全文章

根据短文内容,从短文后的选项中选出能填入空白处的最佳选项,并在答题卡上将该项涂黑。选项中有两项为多余选项。

—*Discoveries Magazine* is looking for a reporter to travel all over the world and write adventure(冒险) articles.

—Oh, it's a good job, I think.

—__31__

—That's right. I've never written a magazine article, but I'm sure I could. __32__

—Oh? What newspaper have you written for?

—Well, so far I've sold articles to the *Chicago Star* and a few other newspaper.

—Have you ever written an adventure article?

—No, I haven't. __33__

—Tell me about one of them.

—Well, once I wanted to report on prisons, so I went to a store and stole something. Of course the police came, and I spent ten days in prison. __34__ When I got out, I wrote two articles about my experiences there. When the public read the articles, they got upset

and complained. ____35____

—That certainly is interesting.

A. It was horrible.

B. So you are interested in working for *Discoveries Magazine*?

C. But I have done some adventurous things to get information for my newspaper articles.

D. Do you like to travel around the world?

E. Since then the prisons have really improved.

F. I've written lots of articles for newspaper.

G. I was put into prison for the second time.

第三部分 英语知识运用

第一节 完形填空

阅读下面短文,从短文后所给的A、B、C和D四个选项中选出能填入空白处的最佳选项,并在答题卡上将该项涂黑。

I grew up in a community called Estepona. I was 16 when one morning, Dad told me I could drive him into a ____36____ village called Mijas, on condition that I could take the car in to be ____37____ at a nearby garage. I readily accepted. I drove Dad into Mijas, ____38____ to pick him up at 4 pm, and then dropped off the car at the ____39____. With several hours to spare, I went to a theater. ____40____, when the last movie finished, it was six. I was two hours late!

I knew Dad would be angry if he ____41____ I'd been in the movies. So I decided not to tell him the truth. When I ____42____ there I apologized for being late, and told him I'd ____43____ as quickly as I could, but that the car had needed major repairs. I'll never forget the ____44____ he gave me. "I'm disappointed you ____45____ you have to lie to me, Jason." Dad looked at me again. "When you didn't ____46____, I call the garage to ask if there were any ____47____, and they told me you hadn't yet picked up the car." I felt ____48____ as I weakly told him the real reason. A ____49____ passed through Dad as he listened attentively. "I'm angry with ____50____. I realize I've failed as a father. I'm going to walk home now and think seriously about ____51____ I've gone wrong all these years." "But dad, it's 18 miles!" My protests and apologies were ____52____. Dad walked home that day. I drove behind him, ____53____ him all the way, but he walked silently.

Seeing Dad in so much ____54____ and emotional pain was my most painful experience. However, it was ____55____ the most successful lesson. I have never lied since.

36. A. lonely B. small C. distant D. familiar
37. A. kept B. washed C. watched D. serviced
38. A. agreed B. planned C. determined D. promised
39. A. village B. community C. garage D. theater
40. A. However B. Then C. Therefore D. Still
41. A. realized B. found out C. thought D. figured out
42. A. went B. ran C. walked D. hurried
43. A. started B. left C. arrived D. come
44. A. word B. face C. look D. appearance

45. A. find	B. decide	C. believe	D. feel
46. A. turn up	B. drive out	C. go away	D. come out
47. A. questions	B. problems	C. mistakes	D. faults
48. A. ashamed	B. frightened	C. nervous	D. surprised
49. A. nervousness	B. sadness	C. silence	D. thought
50. A. you	B. myself	C. me	D. yourself
51. A. where	B. how	C. why	D. when
52. A. meaningless	B. useless	C. helpless	D. worthless
53. A. asking	B. persuading	C. begging	D. following
54. A. physical	B. practical	C. personal	D. natural
55. A. indeed	B. always	C. also	D. almost

第二节　语法填空

阅读下面对话,在空格处填入适当的单词或空格后括号内单词的正确形式,每空填写一个单词。请将答案写在答题卡上的相应位置。

Patient: Hello. I'm here to see Dr. White.

Nurse: What is your name?

Patient: Cameron West.

Nurse: What time is your appointment?

Patient: One thirty.

Nurse: You're a little early. Have a seat in the __56__ (wait) room. I'll call you when Dr. White is ready.

Patient: Thank you.

Nurse: Cameron? Can you come with me? This room is a little more private. Let me take some notes for Dr. White. What brings you here today?

Patient: I have a sore throat that doesn't seem to be going away.

Nurse: I see. Any __57__ symptoms(症状)?

Patient: Yes. It really hurts to swallow and sometimes I lose my __58__ when __59__ (speak).

Nurse: Okay. I'll make a note __60__ your chart for Dr. White. I see it's been a while since your last visit.

Patient: Yes. I've been pretty __61__ (health) up until now.

Nurse: That's good to hear. Your last physical was about a year ago?

Patient: Yes, that seems about right.

Nurse: Well, after you speak with Dr. White, make __62__ to book an appointment for your __63__ (year) physical, okay? You can book it with the __64__ (reception) on the way out.

Patient: Okay. I will. Thank you.

Nurse: Alright then, just wait here. Dr. White is running a bit behind, but he'll be with you __65__ (short).

Patient: Thank you.

Nurse: No problem. Bye for now.

第四部分　写　作

第一节　改写对话

66. 阅读下面对话，根据其内容写一篇介绍 Chinese First Two Astronauts 的记叙文。

要求：

（1）所写短文应与对话内容意义相符，涵盖其要点。

（2）用你自己的语言表达，可改写对话中的句子，但不可照抄原句。

注意：

（1）词数 80 词左右。

（2）请将短文直接写在答题卡上。

Tina：Jim, China sent out another spaceship this morning and this time there are two astronauts in it.

Jim：China has made rapid progress. What are the two astronauts' names? They are so great and lucky to be sent into the space.

Tina：They are Fei Junlong and Nie Haisheng. It is said that they are chosen from a group of astronauts. Before they are sent into the space, they were sent to Russia for training.

Jim：What's that for?

Tina：To help them get used to the life in the space. You know they can't sleep or eat in the space like us on the earth.

Jim：Yes. How long are they going to stay in the space?

Tina：Sorry, I can't remember the number clearly, maybe more than 115 hours.

Jim：Though I know it's very dangerous, I'd also like to go to the space.

Tina：Yes, the two astronauts are chosen because of their excellent physical and psychological states.

Jim：I hope in the future I can also travel to the space.

第二节　书面表达

67. 假定你是李明，毕业于北京新华旅游学校，有一年的业余导游经验，联系电话 62453348。请根据下面这则广告用英语写一封求职信。

HELP WANTED

Friendship Travel Service looking for guides, aged between 20 – 35. Height: 1.65 (female), 1.75 (male); good at spoken English and Putonghua; with a good knowledge of Chinese history, geography and culture. Write to 211 Minzu Road, Dongcheng District, Beijing; 100062. Tel: 68177831.

注意：求职信必须符合招聘广告的要求，可以适当增加细节，使全文连贯；词数 100 左右。

全国英语等级考试
第二级
PUBLIC ENGLISH TEST SYSTEM (PETS)
LEVEL 2

全真模拟卷(2)

第一部分　听　力

第一节

听下面5段对话。每段对话后有一个小题,从题中所给的A、B、C三个选项中选出最佳选项,并标在试卷的相应位置。听完每段对话后,你都有10秒钟的时间来回答有关小题和阅读下一小题。每段对话仅读一遍。

> 例:
> How much is the shirt?
> A. £19.15.　　B. £9.15.　　C. £9.18.
> 答案:C

1. When is Jessica's Birthday?
   A. Sep. 8.　　B. Sep. 9.　　C. Sep. 10.
2. Which hotel does the man live in now?
   A. China Great Hotel.　　B. Holiday Inn.　　C. Hilton.
3. Why will the woman not go to the zoo tomorrow?
   A. The man's son is too young.
   B. She will attend a meeting tomorrow.
   C. It'll snow heavily.
4. Where does the conversation take place most probably?
   A. At a bus stop.　　B. At a railway station.　　C. In a bank.
5. When did the man arrive?
   A. 8:00.　　B. 8:30.　　C. 8:45.

第二节

听下面几段对话或独白。每段对话或独白后有2至4个小题,从题中所给的A、B、C三个选项中选出最佳选项,并标在试卷的相应位置。听每段对话或独白前,你将有5秒钟的时间阅读各个小题;听完后,各小题将给出5秒钟的作答时间。每段对话或独白读两遍。

听下面一段对话，回答第 6 至第 8 题。

6. Where does this conversation take place?

A. In a restaurant. B. In a night club. C. In a supermarket.

7. What kind of snack does the woman have?

A. Pancake. B. Chips. C. Salad.

8. How much does the woman pay for the things she asked?

A. 75 pence. B. 1.30 pounds. C. 2.05 pounds.

听下面一段对话，回答第 9 至第 11 题。

9. Which age group do the two speakers most likely belong to?

A. Young. B. Middle-aged. C. Old.

10. Which part of the body is probably OK with the woman?

A. Her leg. B. Her back. C. Her eyes.

11. Why can't the man do gardening a lot?

A. Because of his back trouble.

B. Because of his leg trouble.

C. Because of his arm trouble.

听下面一段对话，回答第 12 至第 14 题。

12. How does the man feel?

A. Happy. B. Sad. C. Excited.

13. What's wrong with the man?

A. He was knocked down by a car.

B. He had an accident when he was walking along the street.

C. He had an accident in the car.

14. Why did it happen?

A. Because there's something wrong with the driving mirror.

B. Because there's something wrong with the roadside mirror.

C. Because the other driver drove too fast.

听下面一段对话，回答第 15 至第 17 题。

15. Where is Miss Smith?

A. She is at home.

B. She is taking a break.

C. She is attending a meeting.

16. When should Miss Smith call to confirm whether she will attend the meeting or not?

A. On Thursday. B. Today. C. The day after tomorrow.

17. What number should Miss Smith call?

A. 802 8714-246. B. 802 9714-246. C. 902 8741-426.

听下面一段对话，回答第 18 至第 20 题。

18. Why couldn't the speaker meet with Mr. Smith as soon as he arrived?

A. He missed the appointment.

B. He arrived late.

C. He was sick.

19. Why did he give up making a new appointment with Mr. Smith?

A. He couldn't reach Mr. Smith's office.

B. He didn't want to see Mr. Smith any more.

C. He didn't want to take the trouble making it.

20. Whom did he meet on the street one day?

A. A stranger. B. Mr. Smith. C. Mr. Smith's secretary.

第二部分 阅 读

第一节 短文理解

阅读下列短文,从每题所给的 A、B、C 和 D 四个选项中,选出最佳选项,并在答题卡上将该项涂黑。

Text 1

Nobody expected to find them there, outside the city walls. The broken bones of 30 or 40 bodies lay with one on top of the other. It looked bad. There was no sign of battle. Everyone wondered why all these people had died at the same moment. Men came day after day to dig and remove the earth. They worked with great care, like detectives(侦探). Each day something new was discovered. Every bone was studied. Soft brushes were used so that nothing was damaged. It all took a very long time, and there were many puzzles.

Deep in the ground they found an important secret. Below the bodies there was a building made of bricks(砖). Inside it lay the body of a woman. There were many things of value in the building with her—gold for her head, neck and arms, and clothes covered with gold. It was clear that the woman had been a queen. This explained why the other bodies were there. The queen's servants(仆人) had killed themselves immediately after she had died. They wanted to be her servants in the next world too. This all happened 4,500 years ago in the world's first city, Ur of the Chaldees. Usually we learn about the past from books, but man lived for hundreds of thousands of years before any books were written. Only archaeologists(考古学家) can find out about our early history. This story is an example of how archaeologists work.

21. The best title for this passage should be "________".

A. Many Puzzles B. A Very Rich Queen

C. Bodies Found D. Detectives and Archaeologists

22. They believe the people had died at the same time because ________.

A. there had been a battle there

B. the bodies were found outside the city walls

C. the bodies looked bad

D. the bodies were lying on top of one another

23. Which of the following is NOT true?

A. Detectives often work very carefully.

B. Ur of the Chaldees is an ancient city.

C. The queen's servants were killed after she died.

D. We learn the past not only from books but also from archaeologists.

Text 2

Many children act in TV shows. They work several hours every day. So they cannot go to regular(正规) school. How do they get education(教育)?

In Hollywood many TV shows are made. About forty teachers give lessons for the children in the shows. They teach wherever their pupils are working. The teachers' job is very important. They are responsible for(负责) making sure that the children work only the permitted(允许) hours each week. They are also responsible for making sure that children learn the required(需要) subjects. They make sure, too, that the children get enough rest and play, along with their education.

Child-actors are required to attend classes twenty hours each week. California law(法律) says they must be taught from September to June. If they do not make much progress in school, they are not permitted to continue(继续) working in TV shows. TV children are usually good pupils, and most of their teachers like this special kind of work. Their classes are held in some wonderful places. Sometimes the "classroom" is a Mississippi riverboat. Sometimes it is the inside of a spaceship. Often the pupils become famous stars.

24. The child-actors do not go to regular school because ________.

A. they do not get good marks

B. there is no school nearby

C. they have to act several hours a day

D. they have to work all day long

25. The teachers usually hold classes in ________.

A. a classroom building　　B. some interesting places

C. a Mississippi riverboat　　D. a spaceship

26. The teachers' duty is to make sure that the child-actors ________.

A. do not overwork　　B. learn what they must learn

C. have enough sleep and play　　D. all the above

27. The pupils, child-actors, are not allowed to continue working if they ________.

A. do not act well　　B. do not get good marks

C. go to regular school　　D. cannot become famous stars

Text 3

The May Day holiday gives Chinese families a good chance to travel and leave behind the daily routine(日常琐事).

When the seven-day vacation was first put in place in 2000, groups of Chinese tourists went to the mountains to see temples and get off buses to take photos. However, as Chinese travelers diversified(使多样化) their interests, more and more people decided to travel on their own.

Millions of families with their own cars prefer to travel by car.

Cui Xiaotang, a career(职业) woman, and her two friends left from Beijing Saturday in a car. They did not have a firm destination but drove southwards. "Maybe when there is no road for cars, we will stop and stay one night in a local farmer's house," Cui said excitedly about her plan.

Exchanges between north and south and between cities and rural areas are two trends emerging(出现) during the holiday. Northerners can enjoy the beauty of southern rivers, while southerners can travel to cooler parts of the country.

While millions of travelers made their way to Beijing, Shanghai and Guangzhou, people there decided to go somewhere else.

A large number of tourists join groups with plans to travel abroad. Every year, those groups go farther and farther away. There are also those, however, who choose to stay where they are.

Sun Bin, a graduate student representing a large number of "<u>stayers</u>", chose the simplest way to avoid tourist crowds during the holiday. "I'd rather stay in the Beijing Library for the seven days to read National Geographic magazine. I have the whole world in my mind but avoid queuing up in the airport," he said.

28. More and more people would like to travel on their own, because ________.

A. they have more money

B. they have their own cars

C. they don't like traveling with strangers

D. they have their own interests

29. The underlined word "stayers" refers to those who ________.

A. choose to stay where they are

B. choose to stay in the library

C. go home during the holiday

D. stay in Beijing, Shanghai and Guangzhou

30. Which is NOT mentioned in the passage?

A. Some people would like to travel abroad during the May Day holiday.

B. Some people would like to take adventure travel.

C. People with their own cars would like to travel on their own.

D. Some people would like to go to rural areas to have a taste of country lifestyle.

第二节 补全文章

根据短文内容,从短文后的选项中选出能填入空白处的最佳选项,并在答题卡上将该项涂黑。选项中有两项为多余选项。

Henry: Hello, Lourie. How did you enjoy your stay in that city?

Lourie: I enjoyed it very much. __31__

Henry: __32__ what will you do tomorrow afternoon?

Lourie: __33__ Maybe, I'm going to see a friend of mine.

Henry: Well, there's going to be a dancing party at the students' club. Would you like to

come after you meet your friend?

Lourie: __34__ probably with my friend.

Henry: __35__ About four o'clock then.

Lourie: Good. See you tomorrow.

Henry: Good-bye.

A. That would be very nice.

B. By the way,

C. Thank you.

D. How about you?

E. Nothing special.

F. Excuse me.

G. I'd love to,

第三部分 英语知识运用

第一节 完形填空

阅读下面短文,从短文后所给的A、B、C和D四个选项中选出能填入空白处的最佳选项,并在答题卡上将该项涂黑。

The lion once __36__ that he was __37__ unto death and summoned the animals to come and __38__ his last will and testament. So the goat came to the lion's __39__, and stopped __40__ listening for a long time. Then a sheep went in, and __41__ she came out a calf came up to receive the __42__ of the lord of the beasts. __43__ soon the lion seemed to __44__, and came to the mouth of his cave, and saw the fox, __45__ had been waiting outside for __46__. "Why do you not come to pay your __47__ to me?" said the lion __48__ the fox.

"I __49__ your Majesty's pardon," said the fox, "but I noticed the __50__ of the animals that have already come to you; and while I see many hoof-marks going in, I see __51__ coming out. __52__ the animals that have entered your cave come out again I __53__ remain in the open air."

It is __54__ to get into the enemy's __55__ than out again.

36. A. gave in　B. gave out　C. gave for　D. gave up

37. A. sick　B. glad　C. sad　D. dumb

38. A. listen　B. hear　C. hear of　D. learn

39. A. house　B. hole　C. cave　D. shelter

40. A. there　B. the place　C. here　D. where

41. A. when　B. after　C. as　D. before

42. A. last wishes　B. best wishes　C. goods words　D. last word

43. A. And　B. But　C. So　D. Although

44. A. break　B. appear　C. recover　D. comfort

45. A. that　B. which　C. /　D. who

46. A. sometime B. sometimes C. some time D. some times

47. A. respects B. admiration C. honors D. satisfaction

48. A. for B. on C. at D. to

49. A. want B. ask C. beg D. know

50. A. track B. appearance C. way D. print

51. A. some one B. none C. anyone D. nothing

52. A. Till B. As C. When D. After

53. A. like to B. want to C. prefer to D. have to

54. A. worse B. easier C. faster D. harder

55. A. toils B. holes C. pits D. caves

第二节　语法填空

阅读下面对话，在空格处填入适当的单词或空格后括号内单词的正确形式，每空填写一个单词。请将答案写在答题卡上的相应位置。

Server: Hi, Welcome to The Keg. I'm Kelly and I'll be your server. How many are in your group?

Customer: Just me.

Server: OK. Let me get you __56__ (seat). Would you prefer a table __57__ a booth (包间，雅座)?

Customer: I'd like a booth please.

Server: Great! Follow me. Is this okay?

Customer: Yes. Thank you.

Server: Here is your menu. I'll give you a __58__ moments. Can I start you __59__ with a drink?

Customer: Yes. I'll have an ice tea.

Server: Great. I'll be right back with your ice tea.

Customer: Thank you.

Server: Are you __60__ to place your order?

Customer: I'm a little __61__ (decided). Can you recommend anything?

Server: Sure! Our __62__ (specially) today is the grilled sea bass with rice. Although my __63__ (person) favourite is the penne pasta with vegetables.

Customer: The fish sounds nice. Can I get that with a side salad?

Server: It comes with vegetables and rice. I can substitute the vegetables for a side salad or I can add the sided salad as an extra. Which would you prefer?

Customer: I'll have both the vegetables and a side salad.

Server: Great. What kind of __64__ (dress) would you like? We have blue cheese. Balsamic, Italian or Ranch.

Customer: Do you have just plain oil and vinegar?

Server: Yes. I can get that for you, no problem.

Customer: Thank you.

Server: I'll be right back __65__ your order.

第四部分 写 作

第一节 改写对话

66. 阅读下面对话,根据其内容写一篇介绍 Singapore 的说明文。

要求:

(1) 所写短文应与对话内容意义相符,涵盖其要点。

(2) 用你自己的语言表达,可改写对话中的句子,但不可照抄原句。

注意:

(1) 词数 80 词左右。

(2) 请将短文直接写在答题卡上。

Mary: Hi. John. When did you get back from Singapore?

John: Last week.

Mary: What do you think of Singapore? I heard it's very beautiful.

John: Yes. It's a very small but modern country. Now I know why it is called the Diamond Island in the Pacific Ocean.

Mary: Can you describe it in detail?

John: Sure. The environment in Singapore is very beautiful. People there are fond of flowers very much and you can see the flowers along the sides of the roads, in the gardens and squares, etc.

Mary: I heard it's also very clean there, right?

John: Yes. If you smoke in public, you will be fined heavily. You know the rules there are very strict. And the public order is very good. People there are very kind and polite.

Mary: After hearing what you have said, I hope I can also visit there one day.

第二节 书面表达

67. 假设你叫李明,是你班班长。现在是 9 月 15 日下午 4 点 50 分,由于你有急事要外出。你写一张留言条要求赵娜做以下 3 件事:

(1) 本周末彻底打扫好会议室。

(2) 通知所有的英语老师于下周一下午 3 点在会议室开会。

(3) 做好详细的会议记录。

全国英语等级考试
第二级
PUBLIC ENGLISH TEST SYSTEM (PETS)
LEVEL 2

全真模拟卷(3)

第一部分 听 力

第一节

听下面5段对话。每段对话后有一个小题,从题中所给的A、B、C三个选项中选出最佳选项,并标在试卷的相应位置。听完每段对话后,你都有10秒钟的时间来回答有关小题和阅读下一小题。每段对话仅读一遍。

例如:
How much is the shirt?
A. £19.15. B. £9.15. C. £9.18.
答案:C

1. What's the most probable relationship between the two speakers?
   A. They are host and guest.
   B. They are waiter and customer.
   C. They are husband and wife.
2. Where did this conversation take place?
   A. At the hospital. B. At the airport. C. At the post office.
3. Why will the woman go to London?
   A. To have a look at London.
   B. To go with her friend.
   C. To spend the weekend.
4. What's the woman's job?
   A. She is a saleswoman. B. She is a waitress. C. She is a hotel clerk.
5. How is the weather now?
   A. It's snowing. B. It's raining. C. It's clear.

第二节

听下面几段对话或独白。每段对话或独白后有2至4个小题,从题中所给的A、B、C三个选项中选出最佳选项,并标在试卷的相应位置。听每段对话或独白前,你将有5秒钟的时间阅读各个小题;听完后,各小题将给出5秒钟的作答时间。每段对话或独白读两遍。

听下面一段对话,回答第6和第7题。

6. What does the man think the weather is going to be like tomorrow?

A. Rainy. B. Cloudy. C. Sunny.

7. What will the woman probably do tomorrow?

A. Go to the picnic with an umbrella.

B. Stay home because of the rain.

C. Make sure of the weather.

听下面一段对话,回答第 8 和第 9 题。

8. How much money was there in the purse?

A. About \$15. B. About \$50. C. About \$55.

9. Where did the woman most probably leave her purse?

A. In the street. B. In the coffee shop. C. In the shoe department.

听下面一段对话,回答第 10 和第 11 题。

10. Why does the woman look pale?

A. She is probably sick.

B. She feels a bit tired of her work.

C. She works too hard with her new students.

11. What is the relationship between the two speakers?

A. Doctor and patient.

B. Headmaster and teacher.

C. Teacher and student.

听下面一段对话,回答第 12 至第 14 题。

12. What is the woman asking about?

A. How to earn money.

B. How to walk dogs.

C. How to make advertisements.

13. What is the man's first suggestion?

A. Walking dogs. B. Buying a bike. C. Carrying papers.

14. Why does the woman prefer the job of walking dogs?

A. She doesn't have a bike.

B. She can make more money.

C. It's good for her health.

听下面一段对话,回答第 15 至第 17 题。

15. When did the story happen?

A. Early in the morning. B. Late in the afternoon. C. At midnight.

16. What happened to the woman finally?

A. She was killed.

B. She was saved.

C. She was pulled into the water.

17. What kind of person is the woman?

A. Friendly. B. Quick. C. Brave.

听下面一段对话,回答第 18 至第 20 题。

18. What does the speaker mainly talk about?

A. The university library. B. The library rules. C. The library hours.

19. Where is the most likely place to find a book on physics?

A. Level 1. B. Level 2. C. Level 3.

20. How long can a graduate student keep the borrowed books?

A. 14 days. B. 20 days. C. 28 days.

第二部分 阅 读

第一节 短文理解

阅读下列短文,从每题所给的 A、B、C 和 D 四个选项中,选出最佳选项,并在答题卡上将该项涂黑。

Text 1

Baekeland and Hartmann report that the "short sleepers" had been more or less average in their sleep needs until the men were in their teens. But at about age 15 or so, the men voluntarily began cutting down their nightly sleep time because of pressures from school, work, and other activities. These men tended to view their nightly periods of unconsciousness as bothersome interruptions in their daily routines.

In general, these "short sleepers" appeared ambitious, active, energetic, cheerful, conformist(不动摇) in their opinions, and very sure about their career choices. They often held several jobs at once, or worked full- or part-time while going to school. And many of them had a strong urge to appear "normal" or "acceptable" to their friends and associates.

When asked to recall their dreams, the "short sleepers" did poorly. More than this, they seemed to prefer not remembering. In similar fashion, their usual way of dealing with psychological problems was to deny that the problem existed, and then to keep busy in the hope that the trouble would go away.

The sleep patterns of the "short sleepers" were similar to, but less extreme than, sleep patterns shown by many mental patients categorized as manic(疯人).

The "long sleepers" were quite different indeed. Baekeland and Hartmann report that these young men had been lengthy sleeps since childhood. They seemed to enjoy their sleep, protected it, and were quite concerned when they were occasionally deprived of their desired 9 hours of nightly bed rest. They tended to recall their dreams much better than did the "short sleepers".

Many of the "long sleepers" were shy, anxious, introverted(内向), inhibited(压抑), passive, mildly depressed, and unsure of themselves (particularly in social situations). Several openly states that sleep was an escape from their daily problems.

21. Many "short sleepers" are likely to hold the view that ________.

A. sleep is a withdrawal from the reality

B. sleep interferes with their sound judgment

C. sleep is the least expensive item on their routine program

D. sleep is the best way to deal with psychological troubles

22. It is stated in the third paragraph that short sleepers ________.

A. are ideally vigorous even under the pressures of life

B. often neglect the consequences of inadequate sleep

C. do not know how to relax properly

D. are more unlikely to run into mental problems

23. Which of the following is NOT included in the passage?

A. If one sleeps inadequately, his performance suffers and his memory is weakened.

B. The sleep patterns of short sleepers are exactly the same as those shown by many mental patients.

C. Long and short sleepers differ in their attitudes towards sleep.

D. Short sleepers would be better off with more rest.

Text 2

Until the 1980s, the American homeless population comprised mainly older males. Today, homelessness strikes much younger part of society. In fact, a 25-city survey by the US Conference of Mayors in 1987 found that families with children make up the fastest growing part of the homeless population. Many homeless children gather in inner cities; this transient(变化无常的) and frequently frightened student population creates additional problems—both legal and educational—for already overburdened urban school administrators and teachers.

Estimates of the number of homeless Americans range from 350,000 to three million. Likewise, estimates of the number of homeless school children vary radically. A US Department of Education report, based on state estimates, states that there are 220,000 homeless school-age children, about a third of whom do not attend school on a regular basis, But the National Coalition for the Homeless estimates that there are at least two times as many homeless children, and that less than half of them attend school regularly.

One part of the homeless population that is particularly difficult to count consists of the "throwaway" youths who have been cast of their homes. The Elementary School Center in New York City estimates that there are 1.5 million of them, many of whom are not counted as children because they do not stay in family shelters and tend to live by themselves on the streets.

Federal law, the Stewart B. McKinney Homeless Assistance Act of 1987, includes a section that addresses the educational needs of homeless children. The educational provisions of the McKinney Act are based on the belief that all homeless children have the right to a free, appropriate education.

24. It is implied in the first paragraph that ________.

A. the writer himself is homeless, even in his eighties

B. many older homeless residents are going on strike in 25 cities

C. there is a serious shortage of academic facilities

D. homeless children are denied the opportunity of receiving free education

25. The National Coalition for the homeless believes that the number of homeless children is ________.

A. 350,000 B. 1,500,000 C. 440,000 D. 110,000

26. The passage mainly deals with ________.

A. the legal problems of the homeless children

B. the educational problems of homeless children

C. the social status of older males

D. estimates on the homeless population

Text 3

Speeding off in a stolen car, the thief thinks he has got a great catch. But he is in for an unwelcome surprise. The car is fitted with a remote immobilizer(锁止器), and a radio signal from a control centre miles away will ensure that once the thief switches the engine off, he will not be able to start it again.

The idea goes like this. A control box fitted to the car contains a mini-cell-phone, a microprocessor and memory, and a GPS(全球定位系统) satellite positioning receiver. If the car is stolen, a coded cell-phone signal will tell the control centre to block the vehicle's engine management system and prevent the engine being restarted.

In the UK, a set of technical fixes is already making life harder for car thieves. "The pattern of vehicle crime has changed," says Martyn Randall, a security expert. He says it would only take him a few minutes to teach a person how to steal a car, using a bare minimum of tools, but only if the car is more than 10 years old.

Modern cars are far tougher to steal, as their engine management computer won't allow them to start unless they receive a unique ID code beamed out by the ignition(点火) key. In the UK, technologies like this have helped achieve a 31% drop in vehicle-related crime since 1997.

But determined criminals are still managing to find other ways to steal cars, often by getting hold of the owner's keys. And key theft is responsible for 40% of the thefts of vehicles fitted with a tracking system.

If the car travels 100 meters without the driver confirming their ID, the system will send a signal to an operations centre that it has been stolen. The hundred meters minimum avoids false alarms due to inaccuracies in the GPS signal.

Staff at the centre will then contact the owner to confirm that the car really is missing, and keep police informed of the vehicle's movements via the car's GPS unit.

27. What's the function of the remote immobilizer fitted to a car?
    A. To help the police make a surprise attack on the car thief.
    B. To allow the car to lock automatically when stolen.
    C. To prevent the car thief from restarting it once it stops.
    D. To prevent car theft by sending a radio signal to the car owner.
28. By saying "The pattern of vehicle crime has changed" (Lines 1 - 2. Para. 3), Martyn Randall suggests that ________.
    A. it takes a longer time for the car thief to do the stealing
    B. self-prepared tools are no longer enough for car theft
    C. the thief has to make use of computer technology
    D. the thief has lost interest in stealing cars over 10 years old
29. What is essential in making a modem car tougher to steal?
    A. A coded ignition key.
    B. A unique ID card.
    C. A special cell-phone signal.
    D. A GPS satellite positioning receiver.
30. What will the operations centre do first after receiving an alarm?
    A. Start the tracking system. B. Contact the car owner.

C. Block the car engine.　　　　　　D. Locate the missing car.

第二节　补全文章

根据短文内容,从短文后的选项中选出能填入空白处的最佳选项,并在答题卡上将该项涂黑。选项中有两项为多余选项。

—Are you ready for the trip to the museum in Big Apple? I can hardly wait.

—The Big Apple? __31__

—The Big Apple is the nickname(昵称) for New York City. You are going to New York with us, aren't you?

—Yes, I am. I'm especially looking forward to seeing the Museum of Modern Arts. __32__

— __33__ When they played a concert in city, they called the city an apple. Of course, __34__ So the musicians called it the Big Apple.

—Amazing! __35__ And it even has an interesting nickname, one that it had for more than 50 years.

A. Are you making a joke?

B. What are you talking about?

C. New York is such a fascinating place.

D. Big apple taste nice and people like them.

E. It is because of the jazz musicians of the 1920's.

F. But tell me, where does the nickname of the Big Apple come from?

G. New York was the biggest city in the country, and the best place for a jazz concert.

第三部分　英语知识运用

第一节　完形填空

阅读下面短文,从短文后所给的A、B、C和D四个选项中选出能填入空白处的最佳选项,并在答题卡上将该项涂黑。

A young man had been __36__ in a daring act of theft and had been condemned to be executed(处决) for it. He expressed his __37__ to see his mother, and to __38__ her __39__ he __40__ execution, and of course this was granted.

When his mother __41__ him he said, "I want to __42__ to you," and when she brought her ear near him, he nearly __43__. All the bystanders(旁观者) were __44__, and asked him __45__ he could mean by __46__ brutal and inhuman conduct.

"It is to punish her," he said. "When I was young I __47__ stealing little things, and brought them home to mother. __48__ rebuking and punishing me, she __49__ and said, 'It will not be __50__.' It is __51__ her that I am here today."

"He is __52__, woman," said the priest, "the Lord has said, '__53__ a child __54__ he __55__ go; and when he is old he will not depart wherefrom.'"

36. A. killed　B. caught　C. blamed　D. punished
37. A. desire　B. idea　C. thought　D. willing
38. A. discuss with　B. tell　C. speak with　D. talk
39. A. when　B. after　C. before　D. as
40. A. lead to　B. was led to　C. led to　D. was leading to

41.	A. came to	B. came on	C. came up	D. came in
42.	A. tell	B. speak	C. say	D. whisper
43.	A. took it off	B. took it away	C. bit it off	D. got it off
44.	A. horrified	B. surprised	C. angry	D. indifferent
45.	A. what	B. which	C. that	D. how
46.	A. so	B. such	C. very	D. too
47.	A. began to	B. began at	C. began with	D. began
48.	A. Instead of	B. Despite of	C. Although	D. Because of
49.	A. cried	B. was angry	C. was surprised	D. laughed
50.	A. looked	B. glanced	C. seen	D. noticed
51.	A. as	B. because of	C. because	D. besides
52.	A. right	B. wrong	C. fool	D. nonsense
53.	A. Grow up	B. Bring up	C. Pull up	D. Train up
54.	A. in the way	B. on the way	C. by the way	D. from the way
55.	A. can	B. might	C. must	D. should

第二节　语法填空

阅读下面对话，在空格处填入适当的单词或空格后括号内单词的正确形式，每空填写一个单词。请将答案写在答题卡上的相应位置。

Mark: Hi, Peter! How are you doing these days?

Peter: Oh, hi, Mark. I'm not doing very well, actually.

Mark: I'm sorry to hear that. What seems to be the problem?

Peter: ... You know I've been __56__ for work. I can't seem __57__ find a job.

Mark: That's too bad. Why did you leave your last job?

Peter: Well, my boss treated me __58__ (bad), and I didn't like my chances of advancing in the company.

Mark: That makes __59__. A job without opportunities and a difficult boss isn't very __60__ (attract).

Peter: Exactly! So, anyway, I decided to quit and find a new job. I sent __61__ my resume to more than twenty companies. Unfortunately, I've only had two interviews so far.

Mark: Have you tried looking online for a job?

Peter: Yes, but so many of the jobs require __62__ (move) to another city. I don't want to do that.

Mark: I can understand that. How about going to some of those networking groups?

Peter: I haven't tried those. What are they?

Mark: They're groups of people who __63__ (be) also looking for work. They help each other discover new opportunities.

Peter: That sounds great. I'll definitely try some of those.

Mark: I'm glad to hear that. So, what are you doing here?

Peter: Oh, I'm shopping for a new suit. I want to make the best __64__ (impress) possible at my job interviews!

Mark: There you go. That's the spirit. I'm sure things will look up for you soon.

Peter: Yes, you're probably right. I hope __65__ !

第四部分 写 作

第一节 改写对话

66. 阅读下面对话,根据其内容写一篇关于 Pollution of the Yellow River 的议论文。要求:

(1) 所写短文应与对话内容意义相符,涵盖其要点。

(2) 用你自己的语言表达,可改写对话中的句子,但不可照抄原句。

注意:

1. 词数 80 词左右。

2. 请将短文直接写在答题卡上。

Wang: Hi. Zhang. Have you finished the research on the pollution of the Yellow River?

Zhang: Yes. The pollution is much more serious than my expectation.

Wang: I feel sad! How many places have you been to this time?

Zhang: Because of the limited time, we have only been to 5 provinces to investigate the pollution of it.

Wang: What are your finding?

Zhang: Parts of the river are dry now. Some factories still neglect the environmental rules and throw the waste into the river.

Wang: They are killing our mother river.

Zhang: But I also met some students from Mother River Protection Operation. They went to different cities and villages to persuade more and more people to join their movement.

Wang: To protect the Yellow River, we also should plant more trees along the river and try to make the river clean. If everyone can join the movement, our mother river can be saved.

Zhang: Yes, it needs everyone's love.

第二节 书面表达

67. 假设你叫李明,你从报纸上知道一所重点中学招聘英语老师,根据下表给校长写一封自荐信。

姓 名	李 明	年 龄	26	性 别	男
教 育	2005 年毕业于湖南大学外语系				
健康状况	良好				
工作经验	在一所职业高中当了 2 年英语老师				
英语水平	精通				
业余爱好	体育、音乐				
个 性	易相处、喜欢孩子、工作努力、脾气好				

注意:用英文信的书写格式;词数 120 左右。

全国英语等级考试
第二级
PUBLIC ENGLISH TEST SYSTEM (PETS)
LEVEL 2

全真模拟卷(4)

第一部分　听　力

第一节

听下面5段对话。每段对话后有一个小题,从题中所给的A、B、C三个选项中选出最佳选项,并标在试卷的相应位置。听完每段对话后,你都有10秒钟的时间来回答有关小题和阅读下一小题。每段对话仅读一遍。

例:
How much is the shirt?
A. £19.15.　　B. £9.15.　　C. £9.18.
答案:C

1. What is Agatha Christie?
A. A writer.　　B. A bookseller.　　C. A detective.
2. What time is it now?
A. 8:00.　　B. 7:45.　　C. 8:15.
3. Where are the two speakers?
A. Outside a theatre.　　B. In a bank.　　C. At a show.
4. How did the man like the beef?
A. Delicious.　　B. Satisfying.　　C. Not satisfying.
5. What is the man doing?
A. Taking advice.　　B. Making a suggestion.　　C. Asking for permission.

第二节

听下面几段对话或独白。每段对话或独白后有2至4个小题,从题中所给的A、B、C三个选项中选出最佳选项,并标在试卷的相应位置。听每段对话或独白前,你将有5秒钟的时间阅读各个小题;听完后,各小题将给出5秒钟的作答时间。每段对话或独白读两遍。

听下面一段对话,回答第6至第8题。

6. Why was Paul angry with Jane?

A. She told the others about his salary.

B. She told Mrs. Wallace his salary.

C. She always talks to everybody.

7. Why did Jane tell Mrs. Wallace the news according to her own explanation?

A. Because she thought it doesn't matter.

B. Because she knew everybody would know at last.

C. Because she got too excited and wasn't thinking.

8. What does Paul mean by "Everyone in this town got a big nose"?

A. People in this town have big noses.

B. People in this town are always eager to know about others' things.

C. People don't care about each other.

听下面一段对话,回答第 9 至第 11 题。

9. What is the man reading?

A. A magazine. B. A Chinese play. C. A newspaper.

10. Where are they going at the weekend?

A. Beijing Theater. B. Beihai Park. C. Beihai Cinema.

11. What are they going there for?

A. For a visit. B. To see Beijing Opera. C. To learn Beijing Opera.

听下面一段对话,回答第 12 至第 14 题。

12. Why didn't Mike take an examination yesterday?

A. Because he didn't want to do so.

B. Because he got sick.

C. Because he got the examination date wrong.

13. What did the professor permit Mike to do?

A. Have all examination at home.

B. Have an exam sometime later when he got better.

C. Have an exam next term.

14. Why didn't Mike drive his car?

A. Because the doctor told him not to.

B. Because he liked taking a walk.

C. Because he didn't think he was able to.

听下面一段对话,回答第 15 至第 17 题。

15. What does "Rogers" mean in this conversation?

A. Tom's friend. B. Tom's teacher. C. The name of a person.

16. What does Tom tell his mother in yesterday's letter?

A. He had made a new discovery.

B. He had lost his new job.

C. He had just bought a car.

17. Why does Tom tell his mother about his job?

A. Because he doesn't want her to worry about his job.

B. Because he doesn't want her to worry about his life.

C. Because he doesn't want her to worry about his marriage.

听下面一段对话,回答第 18 至第 20 题。

18. Where did the fire probably start?

A. On the first floor. B. On the second floor. C. On the third floor.

19. When was the building built?

A. In 1930. B. In 1782. C. In 1718.

20. What was the building used as at the time of the fire?

A. A history museum. B. A hotel. C. The old people's home.

第三部分 阅 读

第一节 短文理解

阅读下列短文,从每题所给的 A、B、C 和 D 四个选项中,选出最佳选项,并在答题卡上将该项涂黑。

Text 1

Friendship is one of the basic bonds between human beings. While the characteristics of friendship might vary from one country to another, people from all cultures not only enjoy friends but need them.

Many studies have shown that teenagers who have no friends often suffer from psychological disorders. It has been shown that teenagers, perhaps more than any other age group, need companionship and a sense of belonging. The negative consequences of loneliness have also been observed among the elderly. The death of a spouse often leaves a widow or a widower totally bereft. If, however, they are surrounded by friends and relatives and if they are able to articulate their feelings, they are more likely to recover from their grief.

"No man is an island." In other words, we are all parts of society. We all need the love, admiration, respect and moral support of other people. If we are fortunate, our friends will provide us with all of these necessary aspects of life.

As most people observe, there are many levels of friendship. The degree of intimacy of friendship varies depending on the personality of the individuals involved and the context of the relationships. Extroverts enjoy being surrounded by many people whereas introverts are perhaps content with fewer but more intense friendships.

Everyone is not equally open with all their friends. The degree of intimacy is determined by many factors. Close friends can be formed at any stage in one's life but they are usually very rare. Not many people have more than a few really close friends. Irrespective of the level of intimacy, all friendships are based on reciprocity, honesty and a certain amount of love and affection.

21. The second paragraph implies that ________.

A. teenagers without friends will suffer from psychological problems

B. a widow or a widower will die very soon without companionship

C. human beings need companionship and a sense of belonging

D. both A and B

22. "No man is an island" (Line 1, Para. 3) implies that ________.

A. everyone is a part of an island

B. man cannot be an island

C. everyone is just a part of society

D. society is an island

23. The degree of intimacy of friendship mainly depends on ________.

A. age B. belonging C. personality D. culture

Text 2

Many people believe the glare from snow causes snow-blindness. Yet, dark glasses or not, they find themselves suffering from headaches and watering eyes, and even snow-blindness, when exposed to several hours of "snow light".

The United States Army has now determined that glare from snow does not cause snow blindness in troops in a snow-covered country. Rather, a man's eyes frequently find nothing to focus on in a broad expanse of barren snow-covered terrain. So his gaze continually shifts and jumps back and forth over the entire landscape in search of something to look at. Finding nothing, hour after hour, the eyes never stop searching and the eyeballs become sore and the eye muscles ache. Nature offsets this irritation by producing more fluid which covers the eyeball. The fluid covers the eyeball in increasing quantity until vision blurs, then is obscured, and the result is total, even though temporary, snow-blindness.

Experiments led the Army to a simple method of overcoming this problem. Scouts ahead of a main body of troops are trained to shake snow from evergreen bushes, creating a dotted line as they cross completely snow-covered landscape. Even the scouts themselves throw lightweight, dark colored objects ahead on which they too can focus. The men following can then see something. Their gaze is arrested. Their eyes focus on a bush and having found something to see, stop scouring the snow-blanketed landscape. By focusing their attention on one object at a time, the men can cross the snow without becoming hopelessly snow-blind or lost. In this way the problem of crossing a solid white terrain is overcome.

24. When the eyes are sore tears are produced to ________.

A. clear the vision

B. remedy snow-blindness

C. ease the irritation

D. loosen the muscles

25. Snow-blindness may be avoided by ________.

A. concentrating to the solid white terrain

B. searching for something to look at in snow-covered terrain

C. providing the eyes with something to focus on

D. covering the eyeballs with fluid

26. The scouts shake snow from evergreen bushes in order to ________.

A. bide the men behind something to see

B. beautify the landscape

C. warm themselves in the cold

D. prevent the men behind from losing their way

Text 3

We use both words and gestures to express our feelings, but the problem is that these words and gestures can be understood in different ways.

It is true that a smile means the same thing in any language. So does laughter or crying. There are also a number of striking similarities in the way different animals show the same feelings. Dogs, tigers and humans, for example, often show their teeth when they are angry. This is probably because they are born with those behavior patterns.

Fear is another emotion that is shown in much the same way all over the world. In Chinese and in English literature, a phrase like "he went pale and begin to tremble" suggests that the man is either very afraid or he has just got a very big shock. However, "He opened his eyes wide" is used to suggest anger in Chinese whereas in English it means surprise. In Chinese surprise can be described in a phrase like "they stretched out their tongues"! Sticking out your tongue in English is an insulting gesture or expresses strong dislike.

Even in the same culture, people differ in ability to understand and express feelings. Experiments in America have shown that women are usually better than men at recognizing fear, anger, love and happiness on people's faces. Other studies show that older people usually find it easier to recognize or understand body language than younger people do.

27. According to the passage, ________.

A. we can hardly understand what people's gestures mean

B. we cannot often be sure what people mean when they describe their feelings in words or gestures

C. words can be better understand by older people

D. gestures can be understand by most of the people while words can not

28. People's facial expressions may be misunderstood because ________.

A. people of different ages may have different understanding

B. people have different cultures

C. people of different sex may understand a gesture in a different way

D. people of different countries speak different languages

29. From this passage, we can conclude ________.

A. words are used as frequently as gestures

B. words are often found difficult to understand

C. words and gestures are both used in expressing feelings

D. gestures are more efficiently used than words

30. The best title for this passage may be "________".

A. Words and Feelings B. Words, Gestures and Feelings

C. Gestures and Feelings D. Culture and Understanding

第二节 补全文章

根据短文内容,从短文后的选项中选出能填入空白处的最佳选项,并在答题卡上将该项涂黑。选项中有两项为多余选项。

—Would you like a cup of coffee, Paul?

—__31__ if you don't mind.

—Fine. __32__

—Yesterday, I went to visit a friend of mine.

—__33__

—Yes, Harry and I talked about a lot of different things.

—What did you talk about?

—__34__ I asked him if he spoke Japanese.

—You didn't ask him if he knew somebody in Tokyo, did you?

—__35__ He said he did.

A. Yes, please,

B. I'd rather have a cup of tea.

C. Well, we talked about languages.

D. Did you see your friend Harry?

E. By the way, where did you go yesterday?

F. Yes, I asked him that question.

G. No, I asked him that question.

第三部分 英语知识运用

第一节 完形填空

阅读下面短文,从短文后所给的 A、B、C 和 D 四个选项中选出能填入空白处的最佳选项,并在答题卡上将该项涂黑。

Imagine __36__ a young police officer walking the streets of San Jose(圣何塞,美国城市), California, one night and getting an __37__ call from a person who speaks __38__ English. You pull __39__ to the location. You have no __40__ what is awaiting you. It's __41__. In the shadows you see a man at the doorstep. He is waving his arms violently, __42__ words you do not understand. Is he the victim of a crime? __43__, has he just committed a __44__? You have no idea! You __45__ for him to place his hands on his head and turn __46__. He just keeps screaming. You shout again. "Hands on your head!" Nothing! He doesn't understand a word you're saying. What do you do?

What you've just read __47__ every night in every major city in the USA. In this case, things can __48__ out all right. The man's young son was having problems __49__. __50__ the policeman's help the child quickly got to the hospital and __51__. After that incident, the young San Jose police officer __52__ Language Line Services with his instructor friend at Monterey's

Defense Language Institute, ___53___ had the vision and goals to help ___54___ the ___55___ barrier (障碍) between all people.

36. A. himself B. yourself C. myself D. themselves
37. A. common B. ordinary C. urgent D. different
38. A. some B. no C. good D. bad
39. A. up B. down C. close D. on
40. A. interpreter B. one C. idea D. thought
41. A. dark B. bright C. hot D. cold
42. A. talking B. protesting C. discussing D. screaming
43. A. Or B. And C. But D. So
44. A. murder B. crime C. suicide D. killing
45. A. talk B. tell C. shout D. cry
46. A. in B. out C. around D. up
47. A. happen B. is happening C. happened D. happens
48. A. turn B. go C. come D. become
49. A. to breath B. with breathing C. in breathing D. breath
50. A. With B. In spite of C. Lacking D. Have
51. A. look after B. was taken care of C. look for D. was take care
52. A. worked at B. launched C. mentioned D. joined
53. A. that B. who C. when D. which
54. A. bridge B. move C. break D. connect
55. A. psychology B. behavior C. language D. mental

第二节 语法填空

阅读下面对话,在空格处填入适当的单词或空格后括号内单词的正确形式,每空填写一个单词。请将答案写在答题卡上的相应位置。

(At a friend's house)

Carol: This is a lovely house!

Martha: Thank you. Carol, we call it home.

Carol: It's very ___56___ (closed) to work, isn't it?

Martha: Yes, it is. I always walk ___57___ work—even when it rains!

Carol: I usually ___58___ the bus. It takes so long!

Martha: How ___59___ does it take?

Carol: Oh, it takes about 20 minutes.

Martha: That is a long time. Well, have ___60___ cake.

Carol: (taking a bite of some cake) This is delicious! Do you bake all of your own cakes?

Martha: Yes, I usually bake something at the weekend. I like having sweets in the house.

Carol: You're a wonderful ___61___ (cook)!

Martha: Thank you, it's nothing really.

Carol: I never cook. I'm just ___62___ (hope). My husband, David, usually does all the ___

63 (cook).

Martha: Do you often go out to eat?

Carol: Yes, when he doesn't have 64 to cook, we go out to eat somewhere.

Martha: There are some wonderful restaurants in the city.

Carol: Too many! You can eat at a 65 (differ) restaurant every day. Monday—Chinese, Tuesday—Italian, Wednesday—Mexican, on and on ...

第四部分 写 作

第一节 改写对话

66. 阅读下面对话,根据其内容写一篇题为 Instructions on How to Clean Out the Files 的说明文。

要求:

(1) 所写短文应与对话内容意义相符,涵盖其要点。

(2) 用你自己的语言表达,可改写对话中的句子,但不可照抄原句。

注意:

(1)词数 80 词左右。

(2) 请将短文直接写在答题卡上。

(3) 文字简明扼要,建议多用祈使句型。

Mary: Hi. John. Are you doing right now?

John: No, nothing especially important. I've just finished Michael's letters.

Mary: Could you give me a hand, please? These files have to be cleaned out. Look at these shelves! They are full! We don't need them now.

John: All right. What can I do for you?

Mary: All the letters that are kept for more than five years can be thrown away.

John: Aren't some of them important?

Mary: A few of them may be important, but most of them are just regular mails asking about products or prices.

John: What about the addresses on the letters? They might be useful.

Mary: They should be checked against the computer mailing list. You'd better write down the addresses.

John: OK. Give me some pieces of paper and a very large wastebasket, and I'll get to start.

第二节 书面表达

67. 假设你是实验高中的学生李明,得知某英文报招聘兼职记者,你有意应聘。请按以下要点给报社写一封自荐信。

(1) 对这个兼职表示感兴趣。

(2) 说明优势:知识面、英语水平、相关经历。

(3) 希望尽快得到回复。

全国英语等级考试
第二级
PUBLIC ENGLISH TEST SYSTEM (PETS)
LEVEL 2

全真模拟卷(5)

第一部分　听　力

第一节

听下面5段对话。每段对话后有一个小题,从题中所给的A、B、C三个选项中选出最佳选项,并标在试卷的相应位置。听完每段对话后,你都有10秒钟的时间来回答有关小题和阅读下一小题。每段对话仅读一遍。

> 例:
> How much is the shirt?
> A. £19.15.　　B. £9.15.　　C. £9.18.
> 答案:C

1. What will the weather be like this afternoon?
   A. Sunny.　　B. Windy.　　C. Rainy.
2. Where does the conversation most probably take place?
   A. In an office.　　B. In a restaurant.　　C. At home.
3. What does the boy want to be in the future?
   A. A businessman.　　B. A lawyer.　　C. A professor.
4. What is the man doing?
   A. Offering help.　　B. Expressing thanks.　　C. Asking for permission.
5. What does the man mean?
   A. He'll deliver the luggage by car.
   B. He won't take the luggage with him.
   C. He doesn't need any help with the luggage.

第二节

听下面几段对话或独白。每段对话或独白后有2至4个小题,从题中所给的A、B、C三个选项中选出最佳选项,并标在试卷的相应位置。听每段对话或独白前,你将有5秒钟的时间阅读各个小题;听完后,各小题将给出5秒钟的作答时间。每段对话或独白读两遍。

听下面一段对话,回答第6和第7题。

6. What's the relationship between the two speakers?
   A. Teacher and student.　　B. Boss and employee.　　C. Husband and wife.
7. What happened to the man?

A. He failed his final test.

B. He was out of work.

C. He gave the students a hard final.

听下面一段对话,回答第8和第9题。

8. What's the probable relationship between the two speakers?

A. Salesperson and customer. B. Old school friends. C. Fellow workers.

9. What do we know about the woman in the dialogue?

A. She is fond of her work. B. She's tired of traveling. C. She is interested in law.

听下面一段对话,回答第10和第11题。

10. Why does the man want to talk to Dr. Perkins on the phone?

A. To discuss something with the doctor.

B. To ask Dr. Perkins to give a lecture.

C. To see him about his illness.

11. What is the doctor doing at the moment?

A. Giving an operation. B. Giving a lecture. C. Having a meeting.

听下面一段对话,回答第12至第14题。

12. Why does the man want to hire a car?

A. To go and see his friends. B. To visit the city. C. To go shopping.

13. What is the rental money for a Santana?

A. 400 *yuan* a day. B. 300 *yuan* a day. C. 200 *yuan* a day.

14. Which of the following is TRUE according to the conversation?

A. The man is on holiday in Shanghai.

B. The man has decided to hire a Santana for 3 days.

C. Jettas are the most popular with the tourists.

听下面一段对话,回答第15至第17题。

15. Where does the conversation take place?

A. At an airport. B. On a plane. C. At a duty-free shop.

16. What does the man think of the prices of the items in the duty-free shop?

A. Very high. B. Low. C. A little high.

17. Which of the following is RIGHT?

A. The man is from the States.

B. The man has arrived in a foreign country.

C. It took him a long time to get through the Immigration.

听下面一段对话,回答第18至第20题。

18. What can we learn about the radio station?

A. It is owned by the English Coffee Shop.

B. It is on Montana at Seventh Street in Santa Monica.

C. It sells advertising time.

19. What will the weather be like?

A. Cloudy. B. Cold. C. Fine.

20. What can we learn about Santa Monica Beach?

A. It is a good place for parking cars.

B. It is a good place for surfing.

C. It is a good place for swimming.

第二部分　阅　读

第一节　短文理解

阅读下列短文，从每题所给的 A、B、C 和 D 四个选项中，选出最佳选项，并在答题卡上将该项涂黑。

Text 1

BORDER

CROSSINGS

While there are no restrictions on the amount of money that you can bring across the border, you must report to both the US and Canadian border services amounts equal to or greater than \$10,000.

PERSONAL EXEMPTIONS(免税) ON PURCHASES

AMERICANS RETURNING TO THE US

Less than 48 hours: \$200 US

48 hours or more: \$800 US duty-free personal exemption.

next \$1,000 US at 3%

Including up to 100 cigars and 100 cigarettes.

CANADIANS RETURNING TO CANADA

Less than 24 hours: \$50 CAN

48 hours or more: \$400 CAN

Including up to 100 cigars and 200 cigarettes.

7 days or more: \$750 CAN

Including up to 100 cigars and 200 cigarettes.

DOCUMENTATION NEEDED FOR

BORDER CROSSING

LAND OR SEA TO THE US (INCLUDING FERRIES)

A valid passport or passport card, or a NEXUS card.

(A NEXUS card is a Trusted Traveler Program that provides quick travel for pre-approved, low risk travelers through special lanes.)

A recent Washington State, New York or BC driver's license.

Note: Children 15 years of age and younger require only a birth certificate or copy. (Certified copies are not required but are advised.)

AIR TRAVEL TO THE US

A valid passport, an Air NEXUS card, or a US Coast Guard Merchant Marine Document.

21. If a Canadian who is on a 7-day trip to New York buys \$800 CAN worth of goods, how much should he pay tax on when returning home?

A. \$800 CAN.　　B. \$750 CAN.　　C. \$400 CAN.　　D. \$50 CAN.

22. For an American citizen on a 2-day tour of Canada, how much tax does he have to pay on \$1,600 US worth of purchases when returning to the US?

A. $24 US. B. $48 US. C. $52 US. D. $200 US.

23. What documentation should a couple with a 7-year-old child carry when they drive a car from Canada to America?

A. A BC driver's license, an Air NEXUS card, and a birth certificate.

B. An Air NEXUS card, a US Coast Guard Merchant Marine Document, and a birth certificate.

C. Two valid passport cards and a certified copy of a birth certificate.

D. A NEXUS card, a US Coast Guard Merchant Marine Document, and a certified copy of a birth certificate.

Text 2

Imagine, one day, getting out of bed in Beijing and being at your office in Shanghai in only a couple of hours, and then, after a full day of work, going back home to Beijing and having dinner there.

Sounds unusual, doesn't it? But it's not that unrealistic, with the development of China's high-speed railway system. And that's not all. China has an even greater high-speed railway plan—to connect the country with Southeast Asia, and eventually Eastern Europe.

China is negotiating to extend its own high-speed railway network to up to 17 countries in 10 to 15 years, eventually reaching London and Singapore.

China has proposed three such projects. The first would possibly connect Kunming with Singapore via Vietnam and Malaysia. Another could start in Urumqi and go through Kazakhstan and Uzbekistan, and possibly to Germany. The third would start in the northeast and go north through Russia and then into Western Europe.

If China's plan for the high-speed railway goes forward, people could zip over from London to Beijing in under two days.

The new system would still follow China's high-speed railway standard. And the trains would be able to go 346 kilometers an hour, almost as fast as some airplanes.

China's bullet train(高速客车), the one connecting Wuhan to Guangzhou, already has the World's fastest average speed. It covers 1,069 kilometers in about three hours.

Of course, there are some technical challenges to overcome. There are so many issues that need to be settled, such as safety, rail gauge(轨距), maintenance of railway tracks. So, it's important to pay attention to every detail.

But the key issue is really money. China is already spending hundreds of billions of Yuan on domestic railway expansion.

China prefers that the other countries pay in natural resources rather than with capital investment. Resources from those countries could stream into China to sustain development.

It'll be a win-win project. For other countries, the railway network will definitely create more opportunities for business, tourism and so on, not to mention the better communication among those countries.

For China, such a project would not only connect it with the rest of Asia and bring some much-needed resources, but would also help develop China's far west. We foresee that in the coming decades, millions of people will migrate to the western regions, where the land is empty and resources unused. With high-speed trains, people will set up factories and business centers in the west once and for all. And they'll trade with Central Asian and Eastern European countries.

24. China's new high-speed railway plan will be a win-win project because ________.

A. China will get much-needed resources and develop its western regions
B. China and the countries involved will benefit from the project in various ways
C. China will develop its railway system and communication with other countries
D. the foreign countries involved will develop their railway transportation, business and tourism

25. According to the passage, the greatest challenge to the new high-speed railway plan is ________.
A. technical issues
B. safety of the system
C. financial problems
D. maintenance of railway tracks

26. Which of the following might be the best title for the passage?
A. New Railway Standards.
B. Big Railway Dreams.
C. High-speed Bullet Trains.
D. International Railway Network.

Text 3

Here is your best chance to travel around the UK in 2012: More than 200 B&Bs (bed & breakfast) across England, Scotland, Wales and Northern Ireland are selected to offer you amazing services for your stay at their lowest prices! Don't miss it. Just collect the vouchers(活动券) in our *B&B Daily* printed from 01/04/2012 to 07/04/2012 and book the stays for your travel following the terms and conditions below:

- The offer includes a room for the night and a breakfast the next morning.
- The offer is of two kinds: £20 per room, valid(有效的) during stay period of 02/04/2012 –31/05/2012 and then again 01/09/2012 –31/10/2012; £35 per room, per night, valid during stay period of 01/06/2012 –31/08/2012.
- The offer is valid for a basic twin or double room only.
- The stay must be booked directly with the chosen B&Bs before 28/04/2012.
- Each voucher can only be used by the holder to book one room for one night.
- If voucher holders book either the £20 or £35 per room per night, any additional services such as lunch, evening meal or activities may require an extra charge. But these are not required in order to take up the offer. Please check directly with your chosen B&Bs to see what extra services are available.
- Vouchers must be presented on arrival. If no vouchers are presented, the B&Bs may reserve(保留) the right to charge at full price for every night of stay.
- Vouchers may not be used together with any other offer.
- The voucher holders must pay for the stay in full at the time of booking. Additional £10 may be paid to confirm(确认) the booking and will be returned on arrival.
- The B&Bs reserve the right to refuse voucher holders' bookings for people under the age of 18.

27. The voucher can be used for a stay at the chosen B&B on ________.
A. 09/01/2012
B. 04/02/2012
C. 01/03/2012
D. 28/04/2012

28. How much should be paid for a two-night stay in October 2012 at a chosen B&B?
A. £70. B. £40. C. £35. D. £30.

29. What right do the B&Bs reserve?
A. To charge extra £10 for bookings with no vouchers.
B. To refuse bookings for guest under the age of 18.

C. To charge at full price for stays not confirmed.

D. To request extra charges as tips.

30. By taking up the offer, the voucher holders can choose to ______.

A. book either a basic twin or double room at the chosen B&Bs

B. have lunch or evening meal without paying extra money

C. use the B&B offer together with other offers

D. book the stays though *B&B Daily*

第二节 补全文章

根据短文内容,从短文后的选项中选出能填入空白处的最佳选项,并在答题卡上将该项涂黑。选项中有两项为多余选项。

Mr. Wang: Excuse me.

Agent: __31__

Mr. Wang: I have a ticket to Tokyo. How can I get there as soon as possible?

Agent: Let's see. __32__ Oh, China Air. That's all right. I'll see what we have this afternoon. Yes, here we are. There's a flight leaving at 2:40, arriving at 5:15. __33__

Mr. Wang: That's fine.

Agent: All right. I'll change your ticket. __34__

Mr. Wang: Here is my baggage.

Agent: Just put it here.

Mr. Wang: Thank you very much.

Agent: __35__ Have a good journey.

A. You are welcome.

B. It's very kind of you to do so.

C. What can I do for you?

D. Do you have a baggage to check in?

E. What airline is it on?

F. Certainly not.

G. Is that OK?

第三部分 英语知识运用

第一节 完形填空

阅读下面短文,从短文后所给的A、B、C和D四个选项中选出能填入空白处的最佳选项,并在答题卡上将该项涂黑。

Anyone who is __36__ in making friends in cyberspace should consider __37__ a(n) __38__ account somewhere __39__ their personal e-mail address. You never know just who you might __40__ while __41__ and developing an e-relationship, so it is __42__ safer to establish an e-mail account at a remote location that __43__ __44__ about your geographical location. Later, after you decide that someone is __45__, you can give him/her your __46__ e-mail address. __47__, would you give your home address to __48__ that you just met?

Remember to be careful giving __49__ your personal information to anyone that you haven't verified yet, __50__ how well you seemed to have "connected" with that person. Make sure __51__ you agree to meet anyone that you have all the facts about him/her, and __52__ someone

else knows where you are going and who you are going to see. Agree to meet only in a(n) __53__ place, and make sure that someone you know has a photograph of the person that you are meeting. Date and __54__ fun, but be careful and don't forget to use __55__ sense!

36. A. made B. interested C. excited D. astonished
37. A. had B. has C. have D. having
38. A. bank B. e-mail C. interesting D. crash
39. A. other than B. except C. more than D. despite
40. A. come across B. come to C. come up D. come out
41. A. looking up B. checking up C. setting up D. standing up
42. A. too B. much C. many D. very
43. A. hides B. includes C. goes D. reveals
44. A. a little B. a few C. little D. few
45. A. trustworthy enough B. enough trustworthy C. trustworthy very D. very worthy
46. A. false B. true C. another D. personal
47. A. All in all B. After all C. Above all D. In all
48. A. no one B. anyone C. someone D. one
49. A. up B. in C. out D. on
50. A. no matter B. what matter C. how matter D. in matter
51. A. before B. after C. when D. as
52. A. which B. what C. that D. it
53. A. private B. open C. close D. public
54. A. make B. have C. enjoy D. get
55. A. common B. usual C. general D. ordinary

第二节 语法填空

阅读下面对话,在空格处填入适当的单词或空格后括号内单词的正确形式,每空填写一个单词。请将答案写在答题卡上的相应位置。

(Two neighbors talking)

Martha: ... What __56__ (horror) weather today! I'd love to go out, but I think it will just continue __57__ (rain).

Jane: Oh, I don't know. Perhaps the sun will come __58__ later this afternoon.

Martha: I hope you're right. Listen, I'm going to have a party this Saturday. Would you like to come?

Jane: Oh, I'd love to come. Thank you for __59__ (invite) me. Who's going to come to the party?

Martha: Well, __60__ number of people haven't told me yet. But, Peter and Mark are going to help out with the __61__ (cook)!

Jane: Hey, I'll help, too!

Martha: Would you? That would be great!

Jane: I'll make lasagna(宽面条)!

Martha: That sounds delicious! I know my __62__ (Italy) cousins are going to be there. I'm sure they'll love it.

Jane: Italians? Maybe I'll bake a cake...

Martha: No, no. They're not like that. They'll love it.

Jane: Well, if you say so... Is there going be a theme for the party?

Martha: No, I don't think __63__. Just a chance to get together and have fun.

Jane: I'm sure it'll be __64__ of fun.

Martha: But I'm going to hire a clown!

Jane: A clown! You're __65__ me.

Martha: No, no. As I was a child, I always wanted a clown. Now, I'm going to have my clown at my own party.

Jane: I'm sure everyone will have a good laugh.

Martha: That's the plan!

第四部分　写　作

第一节　改写对话

66. 阅读下面对话,根据其内容写一篇关于 How to Lose Weight 的说明文。

要求:

(1) 所写短文应与对话内容意义相符,涵盖其要点。

(2) 用你自己的语言表达,可改写对话中的句子,但不可照抄原句。

注意:

(1) 词数 80 词左右。

(2) 请将短文直接写在答题卡上。

Jane: Gill, I just bought some cakes. Would you like to have some?

Gill: What? Some cakes? But Amy told me you were on a diet.

Jane: Yes, but Amy said I could do more exercise instead of eating less food.

Gill: Yes, that's right. Certainly you should lose weight in a healthy way. But the calories in cakes are very high and can make you put on weight easily.

Jane: Oh, terrible. Then what's the healthy diet for me?

Gill: Besides exercise, you should eat more vegetables and fruits to get the necessary nutrition. But remember calories in white meat are low.

Jane: Sorry, what is white meat?

Gill: It includes chicken, fish, sea food and so on.

Jane: I see. Thank you, Gill.

Gill: You're welcome.

第二节　书面表达

67. 假设你是李明,今天是 2012 年 3 月 15 日,你上午去 Eric 家而不遇,写一便条告知以下事情:

(1) 连日下雨,得知星期天将放晴,非常高兴。你和几个好友将于星期天去郊游。

(2) 上午 8:30 在森林公园门口会合,然后去爬山、玩游戏和野餐。下午在附近河里划船。如果有可能还将采摘草莓。

(3) 希望 Eric 能参加,并请他下午 5 点前打电话给个回话。

根据以上内容写一篇 120 词左右的短文。

全国英语等级考试
第二级
PUBLIC ENGLISH TEST SYSTEM (PETS)
LEVEL 2

全真模拟卷(6)

第一部分　听　力

第一节

听下面5段对话。每段对话后有一个小题,从题中所给的A、B、C三个选项中选出最佳选项,并标在试卷的相应位置。听完每段对话后,你都有10秒钟的时间来回答有关小题和阅读下一小题。每段对话仅读一遍。

> 例:
> How much is the shirt?
> A. £19.15.　　B. £9.15.　　C. £9.18.
> 答案:C

1. What is the relationship between the speakers?
   A. neighbors.　　B. Boss and employee.　　C. Doctor and Patient.
2. How many hours does the woman work every week?
   A. 40.　　B. 47.　　C. 50.
3. What is the man?
   A. A waiter.　　B. A clerk.　　C. An airhostess.
4. What would the woman like to drink?
   A. Coffee.　　B. Milk.　　C. Tea.
5. What is important for them to do?
   A. Practice together.　　B. Experience.　　C. Carry out instructions.

第二节

听下面几段对话或独白。每段对话或独白后有2至4个小题,从题中所给的A、B、C三个选项中选出最佳选项,并标在试卷的相应位置。听每段对话或独白前,你将有5秒钟的时间阅读各个小题;听完后,各小题将给出5秒钟的作答时间。每段对话或独白读两遍。

听下面一段对话,回答第6和第7题。

6. Who is "Mr. Rice Guy"?
   A. A famous cook.　　B. An actor.　　C. A dancer.
7. What can we learn about "Mr. Rice Guy"?

A. He is good at cooking.

B. He likes watching dinnertime show.

C. He is learning to cool from his wife.

听下面一段对话,回答第 8 至第 10 题。

8. Where is the man going?

A. To Paris. B. To London. C. To Berlin.

9. How did the man go to Europe in World War Ⅱ?

A. By plane. B. By warship. C. By truck.

10. How soon will the speakers arrive?

A. In 2 hours. B. In 4 hours. C. In 6 hours.

听下面一段对话,回答第 11 至第 13 题。

11. Who is the woman?

A. A sportswoman. B. A mountaineer. C. A pilot.

12. What caused the accident?

A. She hurt her arm.

B. She lost her way.

C. She landed the wrong way.

13. What can we learn about the woman?

A. She is weak.

B. She failed only twice.

C. She'll recover in about two months.

听下面一段对话,回答第 14 至第 16 题。

14. Where is the speakers' apartment?

A. On the top floor. B. On a middle floor. C. On the ground floor.

15. What can we learn about the house?

A. It's far from the street. B. It's well furnished. C. It's pretty small.

16. What are the speakers doing next?

A. Go to see the house. B. Get a repairman. C. Move into the house.

听下面一段对话,回答第 17 至第 20 题。

17. Why is the meeting held?

A. To make the vacation arrangements.

B. To announce the end of the semester.

C. To announce academic projects.

18. What need the students do now?

A. Move their belongings. B. Fill out forms. C. Leave their dorms.

19. Which will be closed during the vacation?

A. The computer center. B. The library. C. The dining halls.

20. Which of the following will be open on regular hours?

A. The post office. B. The gymnasium. C. The college store.

第二部分　阅　读

第一节　短文理解

阅读下列短文，从每题所给的 A、B、C 和 D 四个选项中，选出最佳选项，并在答题卡上将该项涂黑。

Text 1

On April 18, the 100-day countdown to the 2012 Olympic Games in London began. For this year's Games' slogan, the London Organizing Committee of the Olympic Games has chosen the phrase "Inspire a Generation"(激励一代人). It is expected to inspire athletes to do their best, and common people to do better in their daily lives.

The Games are also inspiring lots of tourists to come to London. But if you go there, you'd better try your best to follow British manners and customs. Otherwise, you'll end up in a right mess! Expert William Hanson has given the Associated Press a few tips for tourists on how to act while in the UK. Let's have a look:

Don't talk about money. According to Hanson, British people hate talking about money and it is considered rude to do so. In particular, never ask anyone about their salary.

Afternoon tea. The traditional view of the British sitting down for an afternoon tea is not exact. Few people keep the tradition nowadays.

Give tips—but not in an obvious way. The British favor a quiet "thank you" gift for good service rather than the rigid 16% –20% tip Americans always give. In fact, many British waiters will not feel anxious and nervous if you decide not to tip at all.

Greeting with a kiss. The British are not like their passionate neighbors in France. Many prefer a handshake or a pat on the back to say "hello".

Conversation tip. If you want to be friendly, end a sentence with the word "mate".

21. The underlined word "It" in the first paragraph refers to ________.

    A. London　　B. "Inspire a Generation"

    C. The 100-day countdown　　D. The London Organizing Committee

22. British people think it rude to ________.

    A. have tea in the early morning　　B. ask others about their salary

    C. give a 10% tip to a waiter　　D. shake hands with friends

23. The underlined word "passionate" in the passage means "________" in Chinese.

    A. 冷酷的　　B. 羞涩的　　C. 有激情的　　D. 聪明的

24. When will the London Olympics be held?

    A. On August 18.　　B. At the end of July.

    C. At the beginning of August.　　D. In the middle of July.

Text 2

Teaching Math, Teaching Anxiety

In a new study about the way kids learn math in elementary school, the psychologists at the University of Chicago, Sian Beilock and Susan Levine found a surprising relationship between what female teachers think and what female students learn: If a female teacher is uncomfortable

with her own math skills, then her female students are more likely to believe that boys are better than girls at math.

"If these girls keep getting math-anxious female teachers in later grades, it may create a snowball effect on their math achievements," said Levine. In other words, girls may end up learning math anxiety from their teachers. The study suggests that if these girls grow up believing that boys are better at math than girls are, then these girls may not do as well as they would have if they were more confident.

Just as students find certain subjects to be difficult, teachers can find certain subjects to be difficult to learn—and teach. The subject of math can be particularly difficult for everyone. Researchers use the word "anxiety" to describe such feelings: anxiety is uneasiness or worry.

The new study found that when a teacher has anxiety about math, that feeling can influence how her female students feel about math. The study involved 65 girls, 52 boys and 17 first-and second-grade teachers in elementary schools in the Midwest. The students took math achievement tests at the beginning and end of the school year, and the researchers compared the scores.

The researchers also gave the students tests to tell whether the students believed that a math superstar had to be a boy. Then the researchers turned to the teachers: To find out which teachers were anxious about math, the researchers asked the teachers how they felt at times when they came across math, such as when reading a sales receipt. A teacher who got nervous looking at the numbers on a sales receipt, for example, was probably anxious about math.

Boys, on average, were unaffected by a teacher's anxiety. On average, girls with math-anxious teachers scored lower on the end-of-the-year math tests than other girls in the study did. Plus, on the test showing whether someone thought a math superstar had to be a boy, 20 girls showed feeling that boys would be better at math—and all of these girls had been taught by female teachers who had math anxiety.

"This is an interesting study, but the results need to be interpreted as preliminary and in need of replication with a larger sample," said David Geary, a psychologist at the University of Missouri in Columbia.

25. What is the result of the research at the University of Chicago, according to the first paragraph?
 A. Girls comfortable with their own math skills are better than boys at math.
 B. Girls uncomfortable with their own math skills are not as good as boys at math.
 C. Female teachers' math skills have influence over girl students' math skills.
 D. Female teachers' confidence in their math skills is related to girl's math skills.

26. What is implied in the third paragraph?
 A. Math teachers, like math learners, do not like the subject due to its difficulty.
 B. A difficult subject like math may affect teachers' confidence in teaching the subject.
 C. Teachers are more anxious teaching math than their students learning math.
 D. Math is so difficult that no teachers like to teach it.

27. David Geary thinks that ________.
 A. the study is interesting but it is based on unreliable research process
 B. the research results need to be retested based on a larger sample

C. the research results need to be reinterpreted to be meaningful

D. the study is well based and produces significant results

Text 3

Understanding how nature responds to climate change will require monitoring key life cycle events—flowering, the appearance of leaves, the first frog calls of the spring—all around the world. But ecologists can't be everywhere so they're turning to non-scientists, sometimes called citizen scientists, for help.

Climate scientists are not present everywhere. Because there are so many places in the world and not enough scientists to observe all of them, they're asking for your help in observing signs of climate change across the world. The citizen scientist movement encourages ordinary people to observe a very specific research interest—birds, trees, flowers budding, etc.—and send their observations to a giant database to be observed by professional scientists. This helps a small number of scientists track a large amount of data that they would never be able to gather on their own. Much like citizen journalists helping large publications cover a hyper-local beat, citizen scientists are ready for the conditions where they live. All that's needed to become one is a few minutes each day or each week to gather data and send it in.

A group of scientists and educators launched an organization last year called the National Phonology Network. "Phonology" is what scientists call the study of the timing of events in nature.

One of the group's first efforts relies on scientists and non-scientists alike to collect data about plant flowering and leafing every year. The program, called Project BudBurst, collects life cycle data on a variety of common plants from across the United States. People participating in the project—which is open to everyone—record their observations on the Project BudBurst website. "People don't have to be plant experts—they just have to look around and see what's in their neighborhood," says Jennifer Schwartz, an education consultant with the project. "As we collect this data, we'll be able to make an estimate of how plants and communities of plants and animals will respond as the climate changes."

28. Ecologists turn to non-scientist citizens for help because they need them ________.

A. to provide their personal life cycles

B. to observe the life cycle of plants

C. to collect data of the life cycle of living things

D. to teach children knowledge about climate change

29. What are citizen scientists asked to do?

A. To develop a specific research interest and become professional scientists.

B. To send their research observations to a professional database.

C. To increase their knowledge about climate change.

D. To keep a record of their research observations.

30. What is NOT true of Project BudBurst?

A. Only experts can participate in it.

B. Everybody can participate in it.

C. It collects life cycle data on a variety of common plants.

D. It has its own website.

第二节 补全文章

根据短文内容，从短文后的选项中选出能填入空白处的最佳选项，并在答题卡上将该项涂黑。选项中有两项为多余选项。

Jim: Hello, Jack! Where have you been?

Jack: Watching the 100-meter dash.

Jim: Oh! __31__

Jack: Tom, of course. __32__ He ran extremely well. How's Bill getting on in the high jump?

Jim: Fine! __33__ And it's his turn to jump again. Do stay and watch a while.

Jack: OK! Let's cheer him on. Bill! Well done! He's cleared 1.80 meters!

Jim: Good! Our class has got seven first places already.

Jack: __34__

Jack & Jim: Congratulations, Bill! You really did very well. We are proud of you.

Bill: Thank you. __35__

A. Who jumped highest?

B. Let's go and cheer him.

C. He ran the race in 11.8 seconds.

D. He's just cleared 1.75 meters.

E. Who came first?

F. Your support was a great help.

G. Let's go and congratulate Bill.

第三部分 英语知识运用

第一节 完形填空

阅读下面短文，从短文后所给的A、B、C和D四个选项中选出能填入空白处的最佳选项，并在答题卡上将该项涂黑。

How many dolls can you stuff(塞) into a spare room? The __36__ —2,300—comes from Gali Little and Katie Banman, both 11, and Katie's 9-year-old sister, Sarah. They know __37__ they just did it.

The girls weren't trying to __38__ it into the *Guinness*(吉尼斯) *Book of World Records*. They want to __39__ children who lost so __40__ during hurricanes(飓风) Katrina and Rita.

"My mom and I were __41__ the news and I saw a lot of children, and __42__ of them had any possessions ... I thought they might __43__ a doll to hold onto and tell secrets to," Gali said.

Gali __44__ her idea of collecting dolls with Katie and Sarah, who are friends as well as neighbors, and the project was __45__ way. The girls start their __46__ at their schools first. They also collected __47__ in their neighborhood. The girls were very __48__ with their success. "I thought we would get only about 100 dolls," Sarah said.

When the three-week __49__ time is over, the dolls are shipped to a charity group.

It will then __50__ the dolls to children still in shelters(庇护所) in hurricane-hit areas.

__51__ do the girls feel about kids having new __52__ friends to hold onto because of their actions? "Proud," the three said with one __53__.

This story has a __54__ ending in more than one way. Not only will thousands of kids be getting new dolls, but Gali's mom now also has her spare __55__ back.

36. A. number B. answer C. result D. question
37. A. because B. even if C. unless D. so that
38. A. set B. keep C. put D. make
39. A. understand B. help C. please D. wish
40. A. few B. little C. much D. lot
41. A. writing B. watching C. hearing D. reporting
42. A. none B. some C. most D. all
43. A. get B. buy C. like D. collect
44. A. shared B. told C. gave D. discovered
45. A. by B. under C. at D. off
46. A. travel B. trip C. plan D. study
47. A. clothes B. books C. money D. dolls
48. A. strict B. surprised C. angry D. careful
49. A. collection B. summer C. school D. holiday
50. A. pay B. sell C. send D. return
51. A. Why B. How C. When D. What
52. A. interesting B. friendly C. strange D. special
53. A. hope B. smile C. look D. voice
54. A. happy B. bad C. scared D. beautiful
55. A. yard B. house C. bag D. room

第二节 语法填空

阅读下面对话,在空格处填入适当的单词或空格后括号内单词的正确形式,每空填写一个单词。请将答案写在答题卡上的相应位置。

Bob: We've undertaken so many changes __56__ the past few months, I'd like to get your take on how things are shaping up.

John: There have certainly been some challenges, but I'd say we're on track to hit our targets for the year's end.

Bob: Where do you think our greatest advantage lies in regards __57__ our __58__ (compete)?

John: We're taking __59__ (advance) of the economics of scale. We've been able to reduce our price point, __60__ gives us the competitive edge in pricing.

Bob: Our new supply chain has really been pushed by the top brass. We're also thinking about __61__ (expand) this strategy to other segments(部分) of the market.

John: It's been tough __62__ our competition. They just can't keep __63__. Not only that, but our uniqueness is finally being perceived(察觉,感知) by a wider audience.

Bob: Our breadth(宽度,幅度) really can't be beat. Marketing's also been doing an

excellent job on getting that message out.

John: Our sportswear line combines durability(耐用性), uniqueness and comfort—at an incredibly affordable price. Can't beat that!

Bob: We're also leveraging(促使……改变) __64__ (society) media to get the message out. It's new territory, but we need to continue to hone that message.

John: Social media is an entirely new game. Marketing's brought in some consulting specialists to help us take advantage of these new __65__ (technique).

第四部分 写 作

第一节 改写对话

66. 阅读下面对话,根据其内容写一篇介绍 Project Hope 的说明文。

要求:

(1) 所写短文应与对话内容意义相符,涵盖其要点。

(2) 用你自己的语言表达,可改写对话中的句子,但不可照抄原句。

注意:

(1) 词数 80 词左右。

(2) 请将短文直接写在答题卡上。

Jane: Gill, do you know Project Hope?

Gill: Yes, I know. It's an important measure that our government has taken to help poor children who cannot afford to go to school.

Jane: That's right. And besides our government, many organizations and people have given plenty of money and school supplies, too. Therefore, many schools have been built and a lot of children get the chance to go to school and get knowledge.

Gill: The development of education should be a priority in our country. I think our country has realized the importance of education. It has taken some good measures on education, such as reducing the students' study costs and increasing the teachers' pay. Our government also encourages young teachers to go to poor areas to help children there.

Jane: Maybe we should do our part for it. We could give some pens and books to them through Project Hope.

Gill: Good idea! Let's do it.

第二节 书面表达

67. 假设你是李明,你将要在下个月接待一位来自澳大利亚的学生(Mike),他将住在你的家里。现在,请你写一封 e-mail,向 Mike 告知以下情况:

(1) 你家的住址。

(2) 你家的环境。

(3) 你的家人以及工作、学习情况。

(4) 饮食、起居的方式。

(5) 欢迎他的到来。

全国英语等级考试
第二级
PUBLIC ENGLISH TEST SYSTEM (PETS)
LEVEL 2

全真模拟卷(7)

第一部分　听　力

第一节

听下面5段对话。每段对话后有一个小题,从题中所给的A、B、C三个选项中选出最佳选项,并标在试卷的相应位置。听完每段对话后,你都有10秒钟的时间来回答有关小题和阅读下一小题。每段对话仅读一遍。

例:
How much is the shirt?
A. £19.15.　　B. £9.15.　　C. £9.18.
答:C

1. What is the man doing now?
   A. Fixing his car.　　B. Working to make money.　　C. Planning to get a mechanic.
2. Who is the man?
   A. An artist.　　B. A carpenter.　　C. A house painter.
3. Where most probably are the speakers?
   A. On a train.　　B. In a car.　　C. On a plane.
4. What does the woman mean?
   A. She lost her notes.
   B. The notes are not hers.
   C. Someone has borrowed her notes.
5. What is the woman trying to do?
   A. Go to sleep.　　B. Watch TV.　　C. Ask her iron back.

第二节

听下面几段对话或独白。每段对话或独白后有2至4个小题,从题中所给的A、B、C三个选项中选出最佳选项,并标在试卷的相应位置。听每段对话或独白前,你将有5秒钟的时间阅读各个小题;听完后,各小题将给出5秒钟的作答时间。每段对话或独白读两遍。

听下面一段对话,回答第6至第8题。

6. How does the woman feel at the beginning of the conversation?

A. Relaxed. B. Anxious. C. Upset.

7. What can we learn about Lucy?

A. She's a troublemaker.

B. She's from a rich family.

C. She isn't getting on well with others.

8. What does the man suggest the woman do?

A. Try to find something in common with Lucy.

B. Go to talk with Lucy later.

C. Apologize to Lucy first.

听下面一段对话,回答第9至第11题。

9. Where are the speakers?

A. At a bank. B. At a repair's. C. At a rent-a-car.

10. How much is the base price for a Hyundai Accent for a week?

A. \$135.99. B. \$288.95. C. \$327.94.

11. What can we learn about the woman?

A. She's a model. B. She's over 25. C. She'll travel alone.

听下面一段对话,回答第12和第13题。

12. Where does the conversation take place?

A. At a clinic. B. At a restaurant. C. At a pharmacy.

13. What restaurant did the woman go to first last night?

A. Chinese. B. Italian. C. American.

听下面一段对话,回答第14至第16题。

14. What are the two speakers mainly talking about?

A. Tennis. B. Football. C. Basketball.

15. Which lines are for the single?

A. The outside ones. B. The inside ones. C. The middle ones.

16. Who will serve the ball after a game?

A. The referee. B. The winner. C. The loser.

听下面一段对话,回答第17至第20题。

17. What does the speaker mainly talking about?

A. Pollution. B. Human voice. C. Good old days.

18. What does the saying "you can't hear yourself think" mean?

A. You have head trouble.

B. You are too stressed.

C. It's very noisy.

19. How many ways of reducing harm are mentioned?

A. Four. B. Three. C. Two.

20. What is the main purpose of the speech?

A. To explain scientific knowledge.

B. To call on people to act.

C. To introduce a saying.

第二部分 阅 读

第一节 短文理解

阅读下列短文,从每题所给的 A、B、C 和 D 四个选项中,选出最佳选项,并在答题卡上将该项涂黑。

Text 1

Learning how to fly took nature millions of years of trial and error—but a winged robot has cracked it in only a few hours, using the same evolutionary principles. Krister Wolff and Peter Nordin of Chalmers University of Technology (CUT) in Gothenburg, Sweden, built a winged robot and set about testing whether it could learn to fly by itself, without any pre-programmed data on what flapping is or how to do it.

To begin with, the robot just twitched and jerked erratically. But, gradually, it made movements that gained height. At first, it cheated—simply standing on its wing tips was one early short cut. After three hours, however, the robot abandoned such methods in favor of a more effective flapping technique where it rotated its wings through 90 degrees and raised them before twisting them back to the horizontal and pushing down.

"This tells us that this kind of evolution is capable of coming up with flying motion," says Peter Bentley, who works on evolutionary computing at University College London. But while the robot had worked out how best to produce lift, it was not about to take off. "There's only so much that evolution can do," Bentley says. "This thing is never going to fly because the motors will never have the strength to do it," he says.

The robot had metre-long wings made from balsa wood and covered with a light plastic film. Small motors on the robot let it move its wings forwards or backwards, up or down or twist them in either direction.

The team attached the robot to two vertical rods, so it could slide up and down. At the start of a test, the robot was suspended by an elastic band. A movement detector measured how much lift, if any, the robot produced for any given movement. A computer program fed the robot random instructions, at the rate of 20 per second, to test its flapping abilities. Each instruction told the robot either to do nothing or to move the wings slightly in various directions.

Feedback from the movement detector let the program work out which sets of instructions were best at producing lift. The most successful ones were paired up and "offspring" sets of instructions were generated by swapping instructions randomly between successful pairs. These next-generation instructions were then sent to the robot and evaluated before breeding a new generation, and the process was repeated.

21. Which of the following is the nearest to Peter Bentley's view on the winged robot?

A. The winged robot could never really fly.

B. The winged robot did not have a motor.

C. The winged robot should go through further evolution before it could fly.

D. The robot could fly if it were lighter.

22. What measured how much lift the robot produced?

A. Two vertical rods. B. A movement detector. C. An elastic band.

D. Both B and C.

23. What does "the process" appearing in the last paragraph refer to?

A. Pairing up successful inst ructions.

B. Sending instructions to the robot.

C. Generating new sets of instructions for evaluation.

D. All the above.

Text 2

Football is, I suppose, the most popular game in England: one has only to go to one of the important matches to see this. Rich and poor, young and old, one can see them all there, shouting and cheering for one side or the other. One of the most surprising things about football in England to a stranger is the great knowledge of the game which even the smallest boy seems to have. He can tell you the names of the players in most of the important teams. He has photographs of them and knows the results of a large number of matches. He will tell you, with a great air of authority, who he expects will win such and such a match, and his opinion is usually as valuable as that of men three or four times his age.

Most schools in England take football seriously—much more seriously than nearly all European schools, where lessons are all-important(至关重要的), and games left for private arrangements. In England, it is believed that education is not only a matter of filling a boy's mind with facts in a classroom; education also means character training; and one of the best ways of training character is by means of games, especially team games, where the boy has to learn to work with others for his team, instead of working selfishly(自私地) for himself alone. The school therefore arranges games and matches for its pupils. Football is a good team game, it is good exercise for the body, it needs skill and a quick brain, it is popular and it is cheap: as a result, it is the school's favorite game in the winter.

24. In England football is a game enjoyed ________.

A. only by young people B. only by rich people

C. only by boys D. by people of all ages and classes

25. There is a great difference between schools in England and those in Europe in that ________.

A. European schools take football seriously

B. European schools often arrange football matches for their pupils

C. schools in England care little about lessons

D. schools in England believe character training to be part of education

26. According to the passage, which of the following is NOT true of the football game?

A. It makes people selfish. B. It encourages cooperation.

C. It is good for health. D. It is not expensive.

27. What is the author's attitude towards the football game in England?

A. Critical. B. Positive. C. Negative. D. Doubtful.

Text 3

The benefits of educating girls are numerous—to individual girls both when they are young and when they become adult women, to their future families, and to society as a whole. Education enables women to contribute more fully to the social and economic development of their societies. A girl's education is also an investment in future generations. The more educated a mother is, the more likely are her children—particularly her daughters—to roll and stay in school. The higher level of education attained by women is strongly associated with lower child death. Experts believe more educated women practice better hygiene and nutrition(营养), use health services more frequently, and survive better. Woman with more schooling tend to be healthier themselves. Perhaps reflecting their improved ability to avoid frequent childbearing(分娩)and to take advantage of available health services during pregnancy(怀孕). The educational level achieved by women, like family planning services, has the most powerful influence on family size. The impact of education on family size is strongest and most consistent for women who have completed some secondary schooling. Educating girls is three times more likely to lower family size than educating boys. Education appears to affect family size in many ways. More educated women not only want fewer children than their less educated husbands, but also are more likely to use effective contraception(避孕) successfully and to limit their families to the number of children, which contribute to smaller family size.

Therefore, family size is ideal and child death rates are lowest in countries that combine strong family planning and health programs with high levels of education for women.

28. According to the article, families and the whole society benefit from women's ________.

A. work B. education C. effort D. health

29. According to the article, mother's education has an effect on children's ________.

A. personality B. experience

C. grades in school D. years of schooling

30. Lower death rate of children owes to all of the following except women's ________.

A. good health B. frequent visits to health services

C. better utilization of nutrition D. management of family resources

第二节 补全文章

根据短文内容,从短文后的选项中选出能填入空白处的最佳选项,并在答题卡上将该项涂黑。选项中有两项为多余选项。

Billy: Oh, it's you. I'm just on my out.

Lenny: __31__

Billy: The news really gets around fast.

Lenny: Let me borrow five dollars from you.

Billy: Five dollars? Until when? __32__

Lenny: Come on, if I had a job, I'd lend you five without asking you any questions.

Billy: But you don't have a job, do you?

Lenny: __33__ I go to the employment office every day.

Billy: Why don't you go back home?

Lenny: If I went home, __34__

Billy: That might be better than wandering around Los Angeles.

Lenny: I like Los Angeles. __35__

Billy: Luck? OK, I'll let you have a couple of dollars. Maybe that may bring you your luck.

Lenny: Yes, this will help. Thanks a lot.

A. No, but I'm looking for one.

B. Yes, I have one.

C. I'd have to work on my father's farm.

D. How are you going to pay back?

E. I haven't got a lot of money.

F. I hear that you have found a job.

G. All I need is a little luck.

第三部分 英语知识运用

第一节 完形填空

阅读下面短文,从短文后所给的 A、B、C 和 D 四个选项中选出能填入空白处的最佳选项,并在答题卡上将该项涂黑。

If you do not use your arms or your legs for some time, they become weak. When you __36__ using them again, they __37__ become strong again. Everybody knows this and nobody would think of __38__ this fact. __39__ there are many people who do not __40__ to know that memory works in the __41__ way.

__42__ someone says that he has a good memory; he __43__ means that he __44__ his memory by practising exercising it. When someone __45__ says that his memory is poor, he actually means that he __46__ give it enough chances to become __47__. Have you ever __48__ that people who cannot read or write usually have __49__ memories than those who can? This is __50__ those who __51__ read or write __52__ remember things. They have to remember dates, places, names, songs and stories. So their memory is the whole time __53__. So __54__ you want to have a good memory, you should learn from those people, __55__ by remembering what you see, hear, feel and write. If so, you must have a good memory.

36. A. begin	B. go on	C. stop	D. continue
37. A. quickly	B. slowly	C. soon	D. at once
38. A. doing	B. agreeing	C. questioning	D. answering
39. A. Yet	B. Still	C. So	D. Certainly
40. A. want	B. seem	C. get	D. hope
41. A. other	B. usual	C. same	D. opposite
42. A. As	B. What	C. While	D. When
43. A. real	B. actually	C. true	D. then
44. A. wants	B. builds up	C. makes	D. keeps
45. A. again	B. else	C. more	D. once
46. A. do not	B. is not	C. never	D. does not
47. A. poor	B. weak	C. strong	D. healthy
48. A. seen	B. heard of	C. noticed	D. thought of
49. A. worse	B. better	C. more	D. less
50. A. why	B. how	C. because	D. the reason
51. A. used to	B. cannot	C. try to	D. have to
52. A. will not	B. have to	C. refuse	D. cannot
53. A. ready	B. being used	C. busy	D. training
54. A. if	B. that	C. though	D. thus
55. A. please	B. try	C. train	D. enjoy

第二节　语法填空

阅读下面对话,在空格处填入适当的单词或空格后括号内单词的正确形式,每空填写一个单词。请将答案写在答题卡上的相应位置。

Betsy: Hi Brian, this is Betsy. How are you doing?

Brian: I've just returned __56__ the Head Office. The weather is great! Boston is a great city!

Betsy: Have you met Frank yet?

Brian: No, I haven't seen him yet. We __57__ a meeting at 10 o'clock tomorrow morning. We are going to meet then.

Betsy: Have you made your __58__ (present) yet?

Brian: Yes, I made the presentation yesterday afternoon. I was very __59__ (nerve), but everything went well.

Betsy: Has __60__ (manage) given you any feedback yet?

Brian: Yes, I've already met with the sales director. We met __61__ (immediate) after the meeting and he was __62__ (impression) with our work.

Betsy: That's great, Brian. Congratulations! Have you visited __63__ museums yet?

Brian: No, I'm afraid I haven't had any time yet. I hope to take a tour __64__ town tomorrow.

Betsy: Well, I'm happy to hear that everything is going well. I'll talk to you soon.

Brian: Thanks ___65___ calling Betsy. Bye.

Betsy: Bye.

第四部分　写　作

第一节　改写对话

66. 阅读下面对话,根据其内容写一篇关于 David's Travel Plan 的记叙文。

要求:

(1) 所写短文应与对话内容意义相符,涵盖其要点。

(2) 用你自己的语言表达,可改写对话中的句子,但不可照抄原句。

注意:

(1) 词数 80 词左右。

(2) 请将短文直接写在答题卡上。

Linda: What are you doing?

David: I'm making plans for our trip to South America during Christmas vacation.

Linda: Oh, yes. Tell me something about it.

David: We could fly there and I've booked a honeymoon suite at the Hilton Hotel.

Linda: It sounds wonderful!

David: We'll have two days to go around to that beautiful city. And we can rent a car to tour around.

Linda: How exciting!

David: We'll spend our last three days sailing the sea in our houseboat.

Linda: And eat steak in high-class restaurant.

David: Yes. In the evening we can drink wine and go disco dancing in the ballroom near our hotel.

Linda: How nice! I've never been there myself. How long are we going to stay there?

David: One week. Then we'll go straight to New York by air.

Linda: That's great!

第二节　书面表达

67. 假设你是李明,最近参加了一期"澳大利亚英语夏令营"活动。在为期两周的夏令营期间,你住在格林夫妇家中,他们为你提供了吃、住、行、旅游等帮助。请你写一封感谢信给格林夫妇。信的内容应包括以下要点:

(1) 安全到家。

(2) 感谢。

(3) 在澳感受。

(4) 保持联系。

注意:可适当增减细节;100 词左右。

全国英语等级考试
第二级
PUBLIC ENGLISH TEST SYSTEM (PETS)
LEVEL 2

全真模拟卷(8)

第一部分　听　力

第一节

听下面5段对话。每段对话后有一个小题,从题中所给的A、B、C三个选项中选出最佳选项,并标在试卷的相应位置。听完每段对话后,你都有10秒钟的时间来回答有关小题和阅读下一小题。每段对话仅读一遍。

例:
How much is the shirt?
A. £19.15.　　B. £9.15.　　C. £9.18.
答案:C

1. What is the probable relationship between the speakers?
   A. Teacher and student.　　B. Customer and shopkeeper.　　C. Boss and secretary.
2. Where does the conversation take place?
   A. At a school.　　B. At a shop.　　C. At a bank.
3. When will the speakers meet each other?
   A. At 10:00.　　B. At 11:00.　　C. At 9:00.
4. What does the woman do probably?
   A. She's a doctor.　　B. She's a teacher.　　C. She's a shopkeeper.
5. How often does the man play basketball?
   A. Once a week.　　B. Twice a week.　　C. Twice a month.

第二节

听下面几段对话或独白。每段对话或独白后有2至4个小题,从题中所给的A、B、C三个选项中选出最佳选项,并标在试卷的相应位置。听每段对话或独白前,你将有5秒钟的时间阅读各个小题;听完后,各小题将给出5秒钟的作答时间。每段对话或独白读两遍。

听下面一段对话,回答第6至第8题。

6. What day is it today?

A. Tuesday. B. Wednesday. C. Thursday.

7. What happened to the woman yesterday?

A. She was kept waiting for a long time at the bus stop.

B. She took a taxi but still was late.

C. She was ill and went to see the doctor.

8. How long has the woman been in the doctor's?

A. For about two hours. B. For about three hours. C. For about four hours.

听下面一段对话,回答第 9 至第 11 题。

9. What does the man think of the mistake?

A. It's just an ordinary mistake and doesn't matter.

B. It could make him lose an important business partner.

C. It could make him lose a good job.

10. What does the woman advise the man to do?

A. Call his guests and explain the problem.

B. Ask his guests to come in another day.

C. Ask his guests to wait for him in the hall.

11. What can we know about the person who made the mistake?

A. He often forgets what the guests say.

B. He has been fired because of the mistake.

C. He is a green hand in the restaurant.

听下面一段对话,回答第 12 至第 14 题。

12. What are the speakers talking about?

A. New Year's wishes. B. Losing some weight. C. Saving some money.

13. What did the man do last year?

A. He got a good job. B. He stopped smoking. C. He joined a health club.

14. Who wants to have a nice vacation?

A. The man speaker. B. The woman speaker. C. Jeff.

听下面一段对话,回答第 15 至第 17 题。

15. What did the man want to do in the morning?

A. Eat some noodles. B. Boil some milk. C. Feed his cat.

16. How did the man hurt his head?

A. He fell down from a ladder.

B. A can of paint dropped on his head.

C. He knocked his head against a window.

17. What did the doctor ask the man to do?

A. Keep his head clean. B. Keep his arm dry. C. Rest for two days.

听下面一段对话,回答第 18 至第 20 题。

18. How old was John when he won a silver medal?

A. 16 years old. B. 17 years old. C. 19 years old.

19. What can we know about the computer?

A. It helped John learn many computer skills.

B. It had bad effects on John's study and sleep.

C. It helped John with his lessons.

20. Why was John happy in the end?

A. His mother showed him her love and respect for him.

B. His mother helped him control himself.

C. He could play computer games late at weekends.

第三部分 阅读

第一节 短文理解

阅读下列短文，从每题所给的 A、B、C 和 D 四个选项中，选出最佳选项，并在答题卡上将该项涂黑。

Text 1

Sugar is so much a part of our modern life that we only really think about it when, for some reason, we cannot obtain it. It has been known to man for at least 3,000 years, but it has come into common use only in modern times. Until quite recently it was considered as a medicine and as a luxury for the very rich only.

Sugar is, then, very important to our civilization. But what exactly is it? Of course, most of us recognize sugar immediately as the sweet material which we put in coffee or cakes. This common form of sugar is derived from two plants: the sugarcane (a type of grass which grows to a height of twenty feet) and the sugar beet (which grows underground). But there are in fact many types of sugar, and the chemist recognizes hundreds of different varieties, each coming from a different source.

About 90% of the sugar is produced as food. Only 10% is used in industry for purposes other than food production. Yet sugar has great possibilities for use as the basis of chemicals. It can even be used for making plastics. In the future these potential uses will certainly be developed more than in the past.

There are many reasons why we should increase the production of sugar. Most importantly, it is one of the most highly concentrated of energy foods. Thus sugarcane and sugar beet produce an average of 7,000,000 calories per acre. In this way they have the advantage over potatoes which give only 4,000,000, while the figure for wheat and beans is 2,000,000 each. So three acres of land growing wheat, beans and potatoes give only slightly more energy than one acre of sugar.

21. The heading of Paragraph 1 may be "________".

A. What Sugar Is

B. Sugar Through the Ages

C. The Advantages of Sugar

D. Present and Future Uses of Sugar

22. The third paragraph emphasizes ________.

A. about 90% of sugar is used as food

B. only 10% is used in industry

C. sugar is used for making plastic D. future uses of sugar

23. Sugar has been used widely ________.

A. for 3,000 years

B. in modern times

C. quite recently

D. for 300 years

Text 2

Of many problems in the world today, none is as widespread, or as old, as crime. Crime has many forms, including crimes against property, person, and government. Crime, in all its forms, penetrates every layer of society and touches every human being. You may never have been robbed, but you suffer the increased cost of store-bought items because of other's shoplifting and you pay higher taxes because of other's tax evasion. Perhaps your house is not worth as much today as it was a few years ago because of the increased crime rate in your neighborhood, or maybe your business is not doing as well as it used to because tourism is down due to increased terrorism in your part of the world. Whatever you do, wherever you go, you are a victim of crime whether you like it or not, whether you know it or not.

Crime, especially violent crime, has risen to a point where many people are afraid to walk alone in their own neighborhoods, afraid to open their door after dark.

Expert argues whether the number of crimes committed is actually on the rise. This issue is particularly true in cases of family violence, the abuse of husbands, wives or children. Throughout much of history, cases of family violence and neglect often went unreported because of the attitude of society, which considered family matters to be private.

24. Which description about crime is NOT correct, according to the passage?

A. It is the most widespread problem.

B. It has the most distant origin.

C. It has many forms.

D. It has very little to do with ordinary people.

25. "Tax evasion" in the first paragraph means ________.

A. "not paying due taxes" B. "imposing taxes on others"

C. "collecting taxes" D. "paying overdue taxes"

26. According to the author, people became victims of crime ________.

A. only when they are robbed or kidnapped

B. even they are not directly involved in any crime

C. when they witness some crime scenes

D. because they tend to commit certain crime

27. Violent crime nowadays ________.

A. is most widespread B. arouses greatest attention

C. is severer than ever before D. makes people less self-confident

Text 3

Long hours at the screen can cause aching eyes, blurred vision and headaches, experts say. In fact, eyestrain surpasses even wrist pain as the top physical complaint among heavy computer users.

When peering into the computer screen, the eye's focusing muscle is at constant tension. Like any muscle, it feels sore when overloaded. And when someone spends a lot of time looking at something close, the eye muscle can get stuck on the near-focus setting and have difficulty relaxing, leaving the person temporarily nearsighted, a condition called accommodative spasm(痉挛) that can last seconds or hours.

This is why after looking at a monitor all day, some computer workers complain that their distance vision is blurred when they attempt to drive home.

The letters on the screen are not as clearly defined as on a printed page. Take a magnifying glass to your monitor and you'll see the letters, each made up of pinpoint sources of light, have no sharp edges. But those liquid crystal display (LCD) monitors, like those found on laptop computers, are easier on the eyes because they display sharper images.

And studies have shown that when people are working on a computer, their rate of blinking goes down by two-thirds, which can result in dry, stinging eyes. This is especially a problem for contact-lenses wearers.

28. ________ used to be the biggest physical problem that computer users had.

A. Dry eyes　B. Blurred vision　C. Headache　D. Wrist pain

29. LCD monitors are better in terms of eye protecting because ________.

A. they are more expensive

B. they will not blur the user's eyes

C. they bring about no eye problems

D. they display letters with sharp edges

30. Which group of people are most likely to get dry, stinging eyes?

A. Drivers.　B. Doctors.

C. Glasses wearers.　D. Contact-lenses wearers.

第二节　补全文章

根据短文内容,从短文后的选项中选出能填入空白处的最佳选项,并在答题卡上将该项涂黑。选项中有两项为多余选项。

A: Your brother hasn't stopped smoking yet, has he?

B: Not yet.

A: But he will stop. __31__

B: Yes, I gave him some advice just a few days ago. He hasn't looked well for weeks. I told him to go and see a doctor.

A: He's ruining his health, but he won't listen to advice. He always says he hasn't got time.

B: __32__ I can't do any more.

A: Perhaps so.

B: __33__ He's overworked and he doesn't get enough sleep.

A: And he looks very pale. I thought he was going to fall asleep at the meeting. He couldn't keep awake.

B: ___34___

A: He hadn't even shaved this morning.

B: I'll have a chat with the dean about him. That would be the best idea.

A: ___35___

A. And what do you think of smoking?

B. But I'm still worried about him.

C. Well, I've done my best.

D. Yes, but we have time. In fact, we'll probably go there.

E. Yes, he could give him a few days off, couldn't he?

F. He's been working day and night on writing a book.

G. I think he's trying hard this time.

第三部分　英语知识运用

第一节　完形填空

阅读下面短文,从短文后所给的 A、B、C 和 D 四个选项中选出能填入空白处的最佳选项,并在答题卡上将该项涂黑。

Animals ___36___ with each other in ___37___ ways. Some insects such as ants ___38___ smell to tell other ants, "There's food over there." Bees communicate by sight. They ___39___ a kind of dance to tell other bees the ___40___ of a supply of flowers. Many mammals(哺乳动物) such as elephants and whales ___41___ information by ___42___. A ___43___ whale can ___44___ another whale 1,200 km away! We humans use ___45___. Many people ___46___, "Do animals use language, too? Can humans and animals communicate with each other?"

___47___ the 1960s and 1970s, two teachers at the University of Nevada, Beatrix and R. Allen Gardener, ___48___ American Sign Language (ASL) to young chimpanzees(猩猩). They ___49___ their first chimpanzee Washoe. ___50___ age five Washoe knew and used more than 160 signs. With these words, she communicated with ___51___. She also ___52___ herself and other animals. Washoe and ___53___ chimpanzees often put signs together to ___54___ a new word. "Metal hot" ___55___ a cigarette lighter, for example.

36.	A. contact	B. contract	C. communicate	D. connect
37.	A. same	B. different	C. common	D. three
38.	A. have	B. get	C. use	D. own
39.	A. do	B. make	C. act	D. perform
40.	A. situation	B. condition	C. environment	D. location
41.	A. exchange	B. change	C. pass	D. deliver
42.	A. smell	B. sight	C. wave	D. sound
43.	A. certain	B. sure	C. kind	D. definite

44. A. touch　　B. hear　　C. see　　D. smell
45. A. sign　　B. language　　C. words　　D. behavior
46. A. wonder　　B. wander　　C. wonderful　　D. suspect
47. A. On　　B. At　　C. In　　D. Both
48. A. learnt　　B. show　　C. gave　　D. taught
49. A. named　　B. told　　C. asked　　D. spoke
50. A. At　　B. By　　C. Till　　D. After
51. A. animals　　B. chimpanzees　　C. humans　　D. mammals
52. A. signed to　　B. said to　　C. talked with　　D. called
53. A. another　　B. other　　C. the other　　D. most
54. A. form　　B. invent　　C. make　　D. discover
55. A. was　　B. is　　C. were　　D. are

第二节　语法填空

阅读下面对话,在空格处填入适当的单词或空格后括号内单词的正确形式,每空填写一个单词。请将答案写在答题卡上的相应位置。

Betsy: I telephoned you yesterday afternoon but you didn't answer. Where were you?

Brian: I was in another room when you called. I didn't hear the phone __56__ (ring) until it was too late.

Betsy: What were you working __57__?

Brian: I was photocopying a report __58__ I needed to send to a client. What were you doing when you telephoned?

Betsy: I was looking for Tom and couldn't find him. Do you know where he was?

Brian: Tom was driving to a meeting.

Betsy: Oh, I see. What did you do yesterday?

Brian: I met the __59__ (represent) __60__ Driver's in the morning. In the afternoon, I worked on the report and was just finishing when you telephoned. What did you do?

Betsy: Well, at 9 I had a meeting with Ms. Anderson. After that, I did some research.

Brian: __61__ like a __62__ (bore) day!

Betsy: Yes, I don't really like doing research. But it needs to be done.

Brian: I agree __63__ you on that, no research—no business!

Betsy: Tell me __64__ the report. __65__ do you think of it?

Brian: I think the report is a good. Tom believes it's good, too.

Betsy: I know that every report you write is excellent.

Brian: Thank you Betsy, you are always a good friend!

第四部分　写　作

第一节　改写对话

66. 阅读下面对话,根据其内容写一篇介绍 Why Should We Stop Smoking 的短文。

要求：

（1）所写短文应与对话内容意义相符，涵盖其要点。

（2）用你自己的语言表达，可改写对话中的句子，但不可照抄原句。

注意：

（1）词数 80 词左右。

（2）请将短文直接写在答题卡上。

Mary：Are you smoking again, Tom? I heard you've quitted.

Tom：Well, I did, but not stayed for long.

Mary：Why? You know smoking is a bad habit.

Tom：I know, but smoking relaxes me a lot.

Mary：It relaxes you?

Tom：Yes, it really does. Everyone is in a hurry to do all kinds of things. To ease my pressure, I choose cigarettes to relax myself.

Mary：But you can choose other ways instead of it. And people who smoke should realize that not only themselves but also the people around them are all damaged by nicotine.

Tom：You know it is very hard for smokers to quit the bad habit soon. Give me time, Mary. I'll try my best to give up cigarettes gradually.

Mary：What I do know is that many people suffer from disease because of smoking. Tom, don't give any excuse for your smoking, and I hope you quit as soon as possible.

Tom：Well, I will. I promise.

第二节　书面表达

67. 假设你是一次城市规划国际会议的英文会务秘书，名字叫李明，你需要起草一封信，通知即将出席会议的人员下列事项：

（1）会议时间：10 月 12 日 9 点至 14 日下午 5 点。

（2）地点：北京人民大楼会议大厅。

（3）交通：从机场每半小时有机场大巴开往市区，也可乘坐出租车。

（4）入住宾馆：北京饭店和建国门饭店。

（5）联系方式：到宾馆后请联系会务组（电话：70554323）。

注意：可适当增减细节；100 词左右。

全国英语等级考试
第二级
PUBLIC ENGLISH TEST SYSTEM (PETS)
LEVEL 2

全真模拟卷(9)

第一部分　听　力

第一节

听下面 5 段对话。每段对话后有一个小题,从题中所给的 A、B、C 三个选项中选出最佳选项,并标在试卷的相应位置。听完每段对话后,你都有 10 秒钟的时间来回答有关小题和阅读下一小题。每段对话仅读一遍。

例:
How much is the shirt?
A. £19.15.　　B. £9.15.　　C. £9.18.
答案:C

1. Where is Linda now?
   A. In the woman's office.　　B. In the classroom.　　C. In the library.
2. What would the man like to do?
   A. To visit his parents.
   B. To drive to the countryside.
   C. To travel to another country.
3. What is the man going to do?
   A. Talk to more students.
   B. Collect more information.
   C. Work on a research paper.
4. Where can the man get the tickets?
   A. From the club.　　B. From Susan.　　C. From Tom.
5. What does the woman mean?
   A. She is warm enough.　　B. She has to study in.　　C. She likes the idea.

第二节

听下面几段对话或独白。每段对话或独白后有 2 至 4 个小题,从题中所给的 A、B、C 三

个选项中选出最佳选项，并标在试卷的相应位置。听每段对话或独白前，你将有5秒钟的时间阅读各个小题；听完后，各小题将给出5秒钟的作答时间。每段对话或独白读两遍。

听下面一段对话，回答第6和第7题。

6. What is the probable relationship between the speakers?

A. Police officers.

B. Manager and clerk.

C. Shop assistant and customer.

7. What are the speakers going to do?

A. Open a store. B. Make a plan. C. Have a meeting.

听下面一段对话，回答第8至第10题。

8. What's the woman's problem?

A. She missed the wake up call.

B. Her room service is out of order.

C. She is unable to get her breakfast in time.

9. Who is going to deal with the problem?

A. The hotel manager. B. A room attendant. C. The woman herself.

10. How does the woman feel about the service?

A. Sad. B. Content. C. Disappointed.

听下面一段对话，回答第11至第13题。

11. Where does the woman work?

A. In a hospital. B. In a lab. C. On a farm.

12. Which of the following does the woman NOT do as a AHT?

A. Produce medicine. B. Bathe animals. C. Do experiments.

13. What does Doctor Blake say about the woman's work?

A. It's interesting. B. It's unimportant. C. It's helpful.

听下面一段对话，回答第14至第16题。

14. What are the speakers talking about?

A. Sea adventures. B. Vacation plans. C. Life at the Caribbean.

15. What has the woman paid close attention to?

A. Weather reports. B. International news. C. Storm damage.

16. What do we learn about the man's experience?

A. He was caught in a storm.

B. He visited islands hit by storms.

C. He made a voyage two weeks ago.

听下面一段对话，回答第17至第20题。

17. What was the woman's job ten years ago?

A. A director in a company.

B. A college teacher.

C. A writer.

18. Who is the college girl mentioned in the talk?

A. The speaker herself. B. The speaker's friend. C. A clerk in the bookstore.

19. Why did the woman give up her job?

A. she wanted more free time.

B. It was far from what she wanted.

C. College life was much more interesting.

20. How does the woman feel now?

A. Regretful. B. Worried. C. Satisfied.

第二部分 阅 读

第一节 短文理解

阅读下列短文，从每题所给的A、B、C和D四个选项中，选出最佳选项，并在答题卡上将该项涂黑。

Text 1

The first celebrations in honor of mothers were held in the spring in ancient Greece. They paid tribute to Rhea, the Mother of the Gods.

In the United States, Julia Ward Howe suggested the idea of Mother's Day in 1872. Howe, who wrote the words to the Battle Hymn of the Republic, saw Mother's Day as being dedicated to peace.

Anna Jarvis of Philadelphia is credited with bringing about the official observance of Mother's Day. Her campaign to establish such a holiday began as a remembrance of her mother, who died in 1905 and who had, in the late 19th century, tried to establish "Mother's Friendship Days" as a way to heal the scars of the Civil War.

Two years after her mother died, Javis held a ceremony in Grafton, West Virginia to honor her. She was so moved by the proceedings that she began a massive campaign to adopt a formal holiday honoring mothers. In 1910, West Virginia became the first state to recognize Mother's Day. A year later, nearly every state officially marked the day. In 1914, President Woodrow Wilson officially proclaimed Mother's Day as a national holiday to be held on the second Sunday of May.

Today, many celebrations of Mother's Day are held throughout the world. Although they do not all fall at the same time, such countries as Denmark, Finland, Italy, Turkey, Australia and Belgium also celebrate Mother's Day on the same day as the United States.

21. Mother's Day was regarded as a nationwide official holiday in the U. S. in ________.

A. 1872 B. 1905 C. 1910 D. 1914

22. Howe suggested people to observe Mother's Day for ________.

A. peace B. comforting mothers

C. love D. honoring God

23. Javis' mother ________.

A. worked hard to gain official recognition of Mother's Day

B. help start the observance of Mother's Friendship Days

C. wanted to do something to help people recover from the Civil War

D. instructed Javis to start a campaign for Mother's Day

Text 2

With the current mood of global uncertainty and an economic recession, people are likely to suffer from increased stress, depression and anxiety. These psychological symptoms, in a new twist to the old saying of "mind over matter", can lead to actual physical problems.

The mind and the body are integrated system. It's like a web. If one part is disturbed, it will directly, or indirectly, affect another part. Hence, psychological and emotional reactions will trigger physical responses.

When a person feels a threat to his well-being, the brain reacts by releasing chemicals. For example, the adrenal gland in the brain may release adrenaline(肾上腺素) which prepares the body to respond to physical threats. The brain's neuro-chemistry programs a person to react in one of the classic ways: fight, flight or fright.

Are you sleeping well? Are you eating well? Are you working or studying well? Any mental health problem would affect these three areas of behavior. Some people deal with stress and anxiety by turning to religion, others by talking to friends and family. But there are other options.

Exercise is a good outlet. Play a game. Go jogging. You will be concentrating on doing something. There is a target to be achieved and will occupy your mind. Go Karaoke singing and dancing with friends. The worst thing to do is to sit at home and think.

24. What does "mind over matter" in the first paragraph mean?

A. Mind is better than matter. B. Never lose your mind.

C. Mind is more important. D. Think before you act.

25. The mind and the body are ________.

A. irrelative B. isolated

C. interrelated D. interchangeable

26. Which is NOT one of the classic ways that people react to stress?

A. Try to struggle with it. B. Try to escape from it.

C. Become worried. D. Start a fight with others.

27. Which is NOT listed as a way to release stress?

A. Talking to people close to you. B. Believing in a religion.

C. Doing jogging. D. Going to see a doctor.

Text 3

Narcissus was a handsome youth. His lovely face and graceful form were the admiration of all who looked upon him. And he knew it. He was so proud that he thought no one but himself was worthy to see his youthful beauty. Narcissus avoided all company, just roamed the wooded hills every day, madly in love with himself.

When he was delightfully wandering about through the woods one day, a wood nymph(仙

女), Echo by name, caught sight of him. She fell in love with him at once. Joyfully moving down towards Narcissus, she stretched out her loving arms. To her disappointment, however, the young man roughly brushed her aside and went by without so much as a glance at her. The poor nymph blushed and quickly withdrew to a shady spot, following the object of her love with her longing eyes.

Presently Narcissus stopped to drink from a little brook. Kneeling down on the side, he saw a lovely face in the clear water. He smiled and was smiled back to. Thinking that it must be a beauty in love with him, he bent down to kiss her. But as soon as he touched the clear surface the lovely face vanished. The youth was now desperate. Never had he been despised like that before. Day and night, he stayed at the stream without drinking and eating. Before long he died, never suspecting that his nymph was none other than his own image in the brook. The gods took pity on the fair corpse and turned it into a flower bearing his name.

Echo saw all this, slowly she faded away for despised love, until at last nothing remained of her except her voice.

28. The story is most probably adapted from ________.

A. legendary stories　　B. fairy tales

C. folklore　　D. Greece mythology

29. Narcissus ________.

A. was deeply in love with himself　　B. refused Echo's love cruelly

C. ran into a beautiful girl at a lake　　D. made friends with Echo

30. It can be inferred from the story that narcissus nowadays refers to ________.

A. a kind of flower growing in water

B. tragic love

C. a kind of flower growing in wood

D. despised love

第二节　补全文章

根据短文内容,从短文后的选项中选出能填入空白处的最佳选项,并在答题卡上将该项涂黑。选项中有两项为多余选项。

Woman: Doctor, I'm not feeling well. I often feel tired.

Doctor: There's nothing much wrong with you, but I'm afraid you have a problem. __31__

Woman: I don't understand! __32__

Doctor: I meant you eat too much food, but you don't take enough exercise.

Woman: Oh dear! __33__ That's a problem. What do I have to do if I want to be thinner?

Doctor: __34__ If you want to be thinner and healthier, you have to eat less food, and you also have to take more exercise.

Woman: What can I eat?

Doctor: Well, every day you can have an apple, an egg, a piece of dry bread, and a glass of milk.

Woman: Thank you, doctor. __35__ Tell me, do I have to take them before or after meals?

Doctor: No! You don't understand! Not before or after meals—instead of them.

A. Is it difficult to be thinner?

B. I want to be thinner.

C. You're eating too much.

D. You meant I'm too fat?

E. No problem!

F. What do you mean?

G. The answer is easy.

第三部分　英语知识运用

第一节　完形填空

阅读下面短文,从短文后所给的 A、B、C 和 D 四个选项中选出能填入空白处的最佳选项,并在答题卡上将该项涂黑。

The Internet use appears to cause a loss in psychological ____36____, ____37____ a research ____38____ the Carnegie Mellon University.

____39____ people who spent just ____40____ hours a week on the Internet experienced more depression(沮丧) and loneliness ____41____ those who spend less time on the Net, the ____42____ study showed. And it wasn't ____43____ people who were already feeling bad spent more time on the Internet, but that using the Net actually appeared to cause the bad feelings.

Researchers are ____44____ at the results, ____45____ were completely ____46____ to their views. They expected that the Net would prove socially ____47____ than television, since the Net allows users to choose their information and to communicate with others.

The fact ____48____ the Internet use reduces time available for family and friends may ____49____ for the drop in well-being. Faceless, bodiless communication may be less psychologically satisfying than ____50____ conversation, and the relationships ____51____ through it may be ____52____.

"But it's important to remember this is not about the technology; it's about ____53____ it is used," says psychologist Christine Riley of Intel. "It really points ____54____ the need for considering social factors in ____55____ of how you design applications and services for technology."

36. A. good-being　B. well-being　C. better-being　D. best-being
37. A. according to　B. depending on　C. because of　D. as
38. A. in　B. at　C. on　D. with
39. A. Even if　B. Even though　C. Even　D. Although
40. A. a little　B. little　C. few　D. a few
41. A. as　B. the same　C. than　D. more than
42. A. two year　B. two-year　C. two years　D. two-year's
43. A. that　B. because　C. for　D. as
44. A. surprising　B. astonishing　C. surprised　D. frightened
45. A. that　B. which　C. who　D. they

46. A. contrary B. contrastive C. different D. same
47. A. healthier B. health C. healthy D. more healthy
48. A. which B. is C. about D. that
49. A. count B. explain C. account D. indicate
50. A. actual B. imaginable C. magic D. ideal
51. A. from B. form C. formed D. forming
52. A. brighter B. lighter C. deeper D. closed
53. A. what B. when C. where D. how
54. A. to B. toward C. at D. in
55. A. terms B. aspects C. parts D. areas

第二节　语法填空

阅读下面对话,在空格处填入适当的单词或空格后括号内单词的正确形式,每空填写一个单词。请将答案写在答题卡上的相应位置。

Susan: Doug, can I talk with you for a moment?

Doug: What can I do for you, Susan?

Susan: I'm __56__ (concern) about the delays we're experiencing with some of our suppliers.

Doug: We're doing everything to get back __57__ schedule.

Susan: Could you give me an approximate timeline?

Doug: A number of deliveries are arriving tomorrow. __58__ (unfortunate), this time of year is often __59__ (trouble).

Susan: That's not good. We can't make __60__ (excuse) to our clients. Are all shipments affected?

Doug: No, but it is summer and some companies are cutting __61__ until September.

Susan: Where are most of our suppliers located?

Doug: Well, most of them are in China, but there are a few in California.

Susan: How does that affect __62__ (deliver)?

Doug: Well, there are weather delays and shipment delays due to reduced production. Sometimes, larger packages are delayed because of a bottleneck at the __63__ (distribute) point.

Susan: Is there any way around these delays?

Doug: Well, we often work with delivery __64__ (serve) such as UPS, FedEx or DHL for our most __65__ (urgency) shipping. They guarantee door-to-door deliveries within 48 hours.

Susan: Are they expensive?

Doug: Yes, they're very expensive at that cuts into our bottom line.

第四部分 写 作

第一节 改写对话

66. 阅读下面对话,根据其内容写一篇关于 Global Positioning System 的说明文。

要求:

(1) 所写短文应与对话内容意义相符,涵盖其要点。

(2) 用你自己的语言表达,可改写对话中的句子,但不可照抄原句。

注意:

(1) 词数 80 词左右。

(2) 请将短文直接写在答题卡上。

Mark: Have you heard about the Global Positioning System for locating things?

Thomas: Yes, I have. It operates through the use of 24 satellites that are circling the earth. The satellites send over their location and time 1,000 times a second.

Mark: That's great!

Thomas: The computer on earth receives this information from several satellites and with that information it will find your exact position.

Mark: Once a friend of mine rented a car at the airport that has an electric map connected to GPS receiver. He said he just gave it his hotel's address then the system showed the fastest way.

Thomas: That's very convenient.

Mark: And it was first used by an engineer whose car stopped in a parking place. His call for help was received by a safety department. And within minutes a truck was there for help.

Thomas: This system has been used successfully in wartime too, during the Gulf War and the Iraq War.

Thomas: Yes, it needs everyone's love.

第二节 书面表达

67. 假设你是李明,你买了一本汉英词典,发现有质量问题,回去调换时售货员的态度不好,因此你给书店经理写信反映这个情况,希望事情得到妥善处理。信中需要包括以下内容:

(1) 事情的起因。

(2) 与售货员交涉的经过。

(3) 呼吁服务行业必须提高服务质量。

全国英语等级考试
第二级
PUBLIC ENGLISH TEST SYSTEM (PETS)
LEVEL 2

全真模拟卷(10)

第一部分 听 力

第一节

听下面5段对话。每段对话后有一个小题,从题中所给的A、B、C三个选项中选出最佳选项,并标在试卷的相应位置。听完每段对话后,你都有10秒钟的时间来回答有关小题和阅读下一小题。每段对话仅读一遍。

> 例:
> How much is the shirt?
> A. £19.15. B. £9.15. C. £9.18.
> 答案:C

1. What's the man doing?
   A. Making a suggestion. B. Making an apology. C. Making an excuse.
2. What's the speed now?
   A. 55 miles per hour. B. 70 miles per hour. C. 105 miles per hour.
3. What's the woman doing?
   A. Making a pair of trousers.
   B. Trying on clothes.
   C. Leaving a message.
4. How many people are having dinner?
   A. Two. B. Three. C. Four.
5. What does the man mean?
   A. He doesn't feel like eating.
   B. He doesn't care about what to eat.
   C. He doesn't like eating chicken.

第二节

听下面几段对话或独白。每段对话或独白后有2至4个小题,从题中所给的A、B、C三个选项中选出最佳选项,并标在试卷的相应位置。听每段对话或独白前,你将有5秒钟的时间阅读各个小题;听完后,各小题将给出5秒钟的作答时间。每段对话或独白读两遍。

听下面一段对话,回答第6和第7题。

6. Who is the woman?

A. A hotel staff. B. A bank clerk. C. A restaurant manager.

7. Why is the man at the hotel?

A. To hold a business meeting.

B. To eat at the restaurant.

C. To spend a holiday.

听下面一段对话,回答第8至第10题。

8. What does the man ask for?

A. Some quarters. B. 20 dollars. C. Some change.

9. How many 5's will the woman give the man?

A. Two. B. Three. C. Four.

10. What's the relationship between the man and the woman?

A. Shop assistant and customer.

B. Professor and student.

C. Husband and wife.

听下面一段对话,回答第11至第13题。

11. Where did Betty live when she was a child?

A. In Singapore. B. In Britain. C. In China.

12. What made Betty feel especially nice when she was in Singapore?

A. People from India and China.

B. Customs from different countries.

C. Foreign tourists.

13. What annoyed Betty when she was in Singapore?

A. Eating strange food.

B. Meeting different people.

C. Being looked at often.

听下面一段对话,回答第14至第17题。

14. What do we know about the man?

A. He is staying in his friend's house.

B. He is to blame for the stolen things.

C. He is busy with his own business.

15. When did the man leave the café?

A. About 7 pm. B. About 10 pm. C. About 11 pm.

16. What does the man's friend care about most?

A. The TV set. B. The computer. C. The paintings.

17. Who is the woman?

A. The man's wife. B. A policewoman. C. The owner of the house.

听下面一段对话,回答第18至第20题。

18. What does the speaker say about Chinese?

A. It has become a language of business.

B. More people are learning Chinese than before.

C. The number of people speaking Chinese is the largest.

19. According to the speaker, which of the following accepts Esperanto?

A. Poland.

B. The Post Office.

C. International Business Organization.

20. What special example does the speaker give?

A. Esperanto. B. Chinese. C. England.

第二部分 阅 读

第一节 短文理解

阅读下列短文,从每题所给的A、B、C和D四个选项中,选出最佳选项,并在答题卡上将该项涂黑。

Text 1

One of the qualities that most people admire in others is the willingness to admit one's mistakes. It is extremely hard sometimes to say a simple thing like "I was wrong about that," and it is even harder to say, "I was wrong, and you were right about that."

I had an experience recently with someone admitting to me that he had made a mistake fifteen years ago. He told me he had been the manager of a certain grocery store in the neighborhood where I grew up, and he asked me if I remembered the egg cartons. Then he related an incident and I began to remember vaguely the incident he was describing.

I was about eight years old at the time, and I had gone into the store with my mother to do the weekly grocery shopping. On that particular day, I must have found my way to the dairy food department where the incident took place.

There must have been a special sale on eggs that day because there was an impressive display of eggs in dozen and half-dozen cartons. The cartons were stacked three or four feet high. I must have stopped in front of a display to admire the stacks. Just then a woman came by pushing her grocery cart and knocked off the stacks of cartons. For some reason, I decided it was up to me to put the display back together, so I went to work.

The manager heard the mouse and came rushing over to see what had happened. When he appeared, I was on my knees inspecting some of the cartons to see if any of the eggs were broken, but to him it looked as though I was the culprit. He severely reprimanded me and wanted me to pay for any broken eggs. I protested my innocence and tried to explain, but it did no good. Even though I quickly forgot all about the incident, apparently the manager did not.

21. How old was the author when he wrote this article?

A. About 8. B. About 18. C. About 23. D. About 15.

22. Who was to blame for knocking off the stacks of cartons?

A. The author. B. The manager.

C. A woman. D. The author's mother.

23. Which of the following statements is NOT true?

A. The woman who knocked off the stacks of cartons was seriously criticized by the manager.

B. The author was severely criticized by the manager.

C. A woman carelessly knocked off the stacks of cartons.

D. It was the author who put the display back together.

Text 2

Kite flying is the sport of sending up kites into the air, by means of the wind, a light frame covered with paper, plastic or cloth. The frame can be one of many different shapes and is attached to a long string held in the hand or wound on a drum. Kites have a long history of practical application and many different types of kites have been developed to serve various purposes.

The ancient Chinese used bird-kites to carry ropes across rivers and valleys. The current folding kite which will dive excitingly is an improved type of such a kite. With its long flat body and single pair of bird-like wings, it looks just like a large bird in the air. The modern version is usually made of tissue-paper rather than the traditional silk.

Man-lifting kites were developed in ancient times, again by the Chinese, for getting information from walled cities and army camps. In fact, as recently as World War Ⅱ, German U-boats flew kites from their towers to lift people into the air to watch the land. These kites, which are no longer in existence, were made of light-weight cloth. They were much larger and stronger than the Chinese ones. Their design, however, was simply that of the cutter kite. Smaller in size, this type of kite is still very popular as a toy for children, being easy to make with a diamond-shaped frame, no wings and brown-paper covering.

Box-kites are another type of kite found in toy shops today. The first box-kite, named for its box-like body, was developed in the nineteenth century to test theories of flight and this type of cotton-covered kite greatly assisted the success of early aero-plane. These kites are the ancestors of a heavier version of the box-kite, which consists of two main sections, placed side by side. Developed for the peacetime purpose of fishing in strong sea wind, it is the only modern kite described which has practical value. A long-lasting plastic material has to be used for this kite, which carries fishing lines.

24. The ancient Chinese bird-kites were usually made of light frames covered with ________.

A. silk B. paper C. cloth D. plastic

25. The kites used by German U-boats in World War Ⅱ for the military purpose were made of ________.

A. brown paper B. plastic material

C. light-weight cloth D. traditional silk

26. The ancient Chinese man-lifting kites were used ________.

A. to carry ropes across rivers and valleys

B. for the military purpose

C. as toy for children

D. for fishing in strong sea wind

Text 3

Most young people enjoy some form of physical activity. It may be walking, cycling or swimming, or in winter, skating or skiing. It may be game of some kind football, hockey, golf, or tennis. It may be mountaineering.

Those who have a passion for climbing high and difficult mountains are often looked upon with astonishment. Why are men and women willing to suffer cold and hardship, and to take risks on high mountains? This astonishment is caused probably by the difference between mountaineering and other forms of activities to which men give their leisure.

Mountaineering is a sport and not a game. There are no man-made rules, as there are for such games as golf and football. There are, of course, rules of a different kind which it would be dangerous to ignore, but it is this freedom from man-made rules that makes mountaineering attractive to many people. Those who climb mountains are free to use their own methods.

If we compare mountaineering and other more familiar sports, we might think that one big difference is that mountaineering is not a "team game". We should be mistaken in this. There are, it is true, no "matches" between "teams" of climbers, but when climbers are on a rock face linked by a rope on which their lives may depend, there is obviously teamwork.

The mountain climber knows that he may have to fight forces that are stronger and more powerful than man. He has to fight the forces of nature. His sport requires high mental and physical qualities.

A mountain climber continues to improve in skill year after year. A skier is probably past his best by the age of thirty, and most international tennis champions are in their early twenties. But it is not unusual for man of fifty or sixty to climb the highest mountains in Alps. They may take more time than younger men, but they probably climb with more skill and less waste of effort, and their experience certainly equal enjoyment.

27. Mountaineering involves ________.

A. cold　B. hardship　C. physical risk　D. all of the above

28. The difference between a sport and a game has to do with the kind of ________.

A. activity　B. rules　C. uniform　D. participants

29. Mountaineers compete against ________.

A. nature　B. each other

C. other teams　D. international standards

30. Choose the best title for the passage: "________".

A. Mountaineering Is Different from Golf and Football

B. Mountaineering Is More Attractive than Other Sports

C. Mountaineering

D. Mountain Climbers

第二节　补全文章

根据短文内容,从短文后的选项中选出能填入空白处的最佳选项,并在答题卡上将该项涂黑。选项中有两项为多余选项。

A: Dad, they offered me a job at the restaurant, but it doesn't sound interesting.

B: __31__

A: $175 a week.

B: I'd take it if I were you. You 've been looking for a job for two months, and this is the first one you've found.

A: __32__

B: Maybe not. But you need a job, don't you? If I were you, I'd consider trying it anyway.

A: __33__

B: It's possible. But it might take a long time. In the meantime, I don't think you can afford to pass up a job opportunity like this one. __34__ Then, later, you can always move to another job if you don't like this one.

A: __35__ I'll think about it.

A. I don't know, Dad.

B. Did they pay you $175 a week?

C. I advise you to take it.

D. But it doesn't sound interesting.

E. You think it a nice job, don't you?

F. How much will they pay you?

G. But I might find a better job somewhere.

第三部分 英语知识运用

第一节 完形填空

阅读下面短文,从短文后所给的A、B、C和D四个选项中选出能填入空白处的最佳选项,并在答题卡上将该项涂黑。

Jerry was the kind of guy you love to hate. He was always in a __36__ mood and always had something positive to say.

He was a manager in the restaurant industry and he __37__ had several waiters who had followed him around from restaurant to restaurant. The reason the waiters liked to follow Jerry very much was because of his __38__ toward life. He was a natural motivator(激励者). __39__ an employee was having a bad day, Jerry was there __40__ him how to look on the positive side of the situation.

His style really made me __41__. So one day I __42__ to Jerry and asked him, "I don't __43__ it! You can't be a positive person all the time. How do you do it?"

Jerry replied, "Every morning I wake up and say to myself, 'Jerry, you have two __44__ today. You can choose to live __45__ or you can choose to be in a low mood.' I choose the former. Each time something bad happens, I choose to __46__ it rather than be a victim. Each time someone comes to me complaining, I can choose to accept their complaining or I can point out the __47__ side of life. I choose the latter."

"Yeah, right, it's not that easy," I __48__.

"Yes," he said. "__49__ is all about choices. When you cut away all the junk, every situation is a choice. You choose how you __50__ to situations. You choose how people will __51__ your mood. It's your choice __52__ you live."

What Jerry said made me think a lot. Soon, I left the restaurant industry to start my own __53__. Gradually, we __54__ touch, but I often thought of him when I made a choice about life __55__ complaining about it.

36. A. bad B. good C. lazy D. busy

37. A. sometimes B. hardly C. seldom D. often

38. A. background B. experience C. attitude D. behavior

39. A. Since	B. Until	C. Because	D. If
40. A. telling	B. ordering	C. exhibiting	D. leaving
41. A. excited	B. curious	C. ashamed	D. crazy
42. A. went up	B. turned up	C. got up	D. picked up
43. A. mind	B. care	C. hear	D. get
44. A. ways	B. difficulties	C. choices	D. problems
45. A. angrily	B. happily	C. carefully	D. silently
46. A. care about	B. complain about	C. tell from	D. learn from
47. A. nervous	B. dark	C. positive	D. sad
48. A. knew	B. agreed	C. asked	D. declared
49. A. Restaurant	B. Life	C. Business	D. Future
50. A. treat	B. mean	C. plan	D. react
51. A. affect	B. exchange	C. inspire	D. feel
52. A. what	B. why	C. how	D. that
53. A. way	B. business	C. life	D. thing
54. A. lost	B. kept	C. gained	D. got
55. A. so far	B. as to	C. apart from	D. instead of

第二节 语法填空

阅读下面对话，在空格处填入适当的单词或空格后括号内单词的正确形式，每空填写一个单词。请将答案写在答题卡上的相应位置。

(Two friends talking over lunch)

John: I just don't know what to do. She's so beautiful, but I don't know what to say...

Alan: It can't be all that bad. She's just a person like you or me...

John: What should I do? Should I ask her __56__ a date?

Alan: Why don't you go a little more slowly? Just sit down next __57__ her in the cafeteria, or in class. Anywhere. Say, "Hi, how are you?", "My name is John." You know, the simple things.

John: But she'll just turn away.

Alan: No, she won't. She'll say "Hi, nice to meet you." You should be more __58__ (confidence).

John: That's easy for you to say.

Alan: Would you like me to speak to her first?

John: No, you are too __59__ (danger)!

Alan: What? Dangerous? What are you talking about?

John: Oh come on, you know all the girls are crazy __60__ you.

Alan: Please... you're __61__ (joke)!

John: Anyway, what should I do?

Alan: You should go __62__ there now. You should introduce __63__ (you) and have a conversation. It's as __64__ (easily) as that.

John: OK, here I go...

Alan: Good __65__ (lucky). And remember, SMILE!

第四部分　写　作

第一节　改写对话

66. 阅读下面对话，根据其内容写一篇关于 The London Subway 的说明文。

要求：

(1) 所写短文应与对话内容意义相符，涵盖其要点。

(2) 用你自己的语言表达，可改写对话中的句子，但不可照抄原句。

注意：

(1) 词数 80 词左右。

(2) 请将短文直接写在答题卡上。

Jane：Gill, you are from England, aren't you?

Gill：Yes, I am from the northern part of England.

Jane：Well, you do find life here is very different from England. What about the subway in London?

Gill：Beijing subways are much cleaner and brighter than those in London. But the subway stations and lines are fewer than those in London.

Jane：Really? That must be very convenient.

Gill：Yeah, we have a rather convenient subway system. You can get almost anywhere rather quickly on a subway, especially at this time of the day when the traffic is heavy.

Jane：Wow, that's great. There must be many people using the subway system. Then what about the tickets?

Gill：All of the stations are equipped with automated vending machines, which are extremely convenient, allowing you to buy tickets whenever you want. Besides, some subway train even provide smoking cars for smokers.

Jane：Sounds wonderful. Here comes the train.

Gill：Let's go!

第二节　书面表达

67. 假设你是东北大学的学生李明。你的一位外国朋友 John 也想上这所大学。请依据以下内容用英语写一封信，向他简要介绍学校的情况。

生　活	学　习
住校，3 人一间宿舍	阅读量大
离市区 10 里，很少进城	很少考试
校内有商店、邮局、银行	每周写数篇文章(essays)
图书馆	应多练读写

注意：可适当增减细节；100 词左右。

参考答案与精析

全真模拟卷(1)

第一部分 听 力

第一节

1. 此题是推断题。对话中的女士说她不愿意住在大城市,根据男士的问题,可以推断她更愿意住在乡村,所以选 C。

2. 此题是推断题。对话中男士打碎了女士的杯子,男士让女士告诉他在哪买的,可以推断选 A。

3. 此题是细节题。对话中提到了 painting(图画),而且男士说是他儿子给他的圣诞节礼物,所以选 C。

4. 此题是推断题。对话中男士问女士的 roommate(室友)怎么样,女士说很让她生气,可以推断她与室友相处得不好,所以选 B。

5. 此题是推断题。对话中女士在寻找一人,男士告诉她,她要找的人不在这层楼,他在第四层楼,要下楼左转才能到, 可以推断他们在第五层楼,所以选 C。

第二节

6. 此题是推断题。对话中,男士问女士报告打完了吗? 可知选 A。

7. 此题是推断题。女士说她买了三明治在桌子旁吃的,可知选 B。

8. 此题是推断题。男士说: I didn't know you were going to look for a new job. 可知选 A。

9. 此题是细节题。女士说:We have some real problems in this department. 可知选 B。

10. 此题是细节题。女士说:I finished some very interesting research about things people do in their spare time. 可知选 C。

11. 此题是细节题。女士说:I talked to 20 people. 可知选 A。

12. 此题是细节题。女士说:I talked to 20 people and 19 of them watch TV. 可知选 C。

13. 此题是推断题。男士在最后说: It's time for my flight, 可知选 A。

14. 此题是细节题。女士说:No other city has as many good restaurants or as much good music. 可知选 B。

15. 此题是细节题。女士说: I am from a very small town in Pennsylvania. 可知选 A。

16. 此题是推断题。女士说:But you speak English like a native speaker. I didn't have any idea。可知选 C。

17. 此题是细节题。女士说:Because my husband and I both worked and our three children were busy with their studies, 可知是 5 人,所以选 C。

18. 此题是细节题。女士说:For a while the children were still unhappy with the idea. They said they would rather spend the time with their friends playing sports. 所以选 B。

19. 此题是推断题。女士说: First we tried setting fixed days: Mondays, Wednesdays, and Fridays. Gradually, though, they began to see the evenings together as interesting and helpful. We loved a lot. 所以选 C。

20. 此题是推断题。由文章可知,一开始孩子们对于一起吃晚餐是不同意的,但后来 Gradually, though, they began to see the evenings together as interesting and helpful. 所以选 A。

第二部分　阅　读

第一节　短文理解

21. 选 D。本题主要从"Except for lung cancer, mostly caused by cigarette smoking, the incidence rates are leveling off, and in the case of some kinds of cancer are decreasing."的对比角度可知。

22. 选 C。从第一段的后半部分可以推定,一般都是认为癌症是由环境引发的。

23. 选 B。从整个第二段来看,罹患癌症的主要是由生活方式引起的,而不是环境本身。

24. 选 C。从第二段"The harbor of the island was too small and unsafe in a storm."以及全文来看,大家为了抢救 Mrs. Yeung 而寻求外援,小岛上肯定没有避难之处。

25. 选 C。从第三段中得知,Mrs. Yeung 生病,因此大家想帮助她。

26. 选 A。从第三段的"There was a small boat on the island but the waves smashed it when some men tried to put it on the sea."以及第四段来看,本次的台风威力很大。

27. 选 B。从第一段第一句话"lived on an island off the east coast of the New Territories"可知,他们住在东海岸之外,因此当然要往西寻求援助了。

28. 选 B。从第一段的第一句话"Welcome to our small business set-up guide"可得知。

29. 选 D。从对三段的"Determination and originality are key"可知,决断力和原创性是最关键的。

30. 选 C。从造字法中可知,"fore-"是"预先"的意思。

第二节　补全文章

根据上文内容,《探索杂志》在寻求一位有旅游经验且写过冒险文章的记者。

31. 询问是否对这项工作感兴趣。选 B。

32. 说明自己曾经为报纸写过大量地文章。选 F。

33. 说自己为了写文章去体验过冒险的事情。选 C。

34. 上文提到在监狱待过几天。选 A。

35. 讲他写了文章之后的结果,就是监狱得到了改善。选 E。

第三部分　英语知识运用

第一节　完形填空

36. C。本题考查形容词。由文中第二段末的"But Dad, it's 18 miles!"可知村庄距离远,且其他三项均未在原文中有所提示,故选 C。

37. D。本题考查动词。文意是把车送去检修,service 作动词有"修理、维修(机器)"之意。

38. D。本题考查动词。这里是说:我向父亲承诺下午 4 点来接他。promise 有"承诺、答应"的意思。

39. C。本题考查名词。根据本文第二句话可知,父亲让我开车送他去 Mijas,然后把车开去修理厂。故选 C。

40. A。本题考查连词。由上下文的内容可知此处表示转折,however 有"然而"的意思,最符合文意。

41. B。本题考查动词短语。句意:我知道若是父亲发现我是一直在看电影,他会生气的。find out 发现、查明,figure out 计算出、理解、想出,realize 认识到。

42. D。本题考查动词。上文说我因看电影而晚了两小时,可知我是要急忙赶去。故选 D。

43. D。本题考查动词。这里是说:我告诉他我已经尽可能快地赶来了。come 来,符合文意。

44. C。本题考查名词。由下文的 Dad looked at me again. 可知此处是说父亲的眼神让我难以忘记。look 作为名词时有"看"的意思,最符合文意。

45. D。本题考查动词。这里是说:你觉得你不得不对我说谎,这点让我很失望。feel 有"觉得、认为"的意思,最符合文意。

46. A。本题考查动词短语。到时间了,我却仍未出现,于是父亲给汽车修理厂打电话询问情况。turn up 出现、露面,最符合文意。

47. B。本题考查名词。由上下文可知,父亲是在担心出了什么问题。problem 问题、难题,符合文意。

48. A。本题考查形容词。ashamed 惭愧的，frightened 害怕的，nervous 紧张的，surprised 吃惊的。我先对父亲说了谎，后来告诉他真相时自然会感到惭愧。

49. B。本题考查名词。父亲对我采取撒谎的方式感到很难过。sadness 悲伤、难过，符合文意。

50. B。本题考查代词。根据空格后面的内容可知父亲是对自己感到生气，故选 B。

51. A。本题考查副词。原文中说父亲要反省自己在哪些地方错了。where 在此处是“在……的地方”的意思，符合文意。

52. B。本题考查形容词。由本段最后两句话可知我的反对和道歉是“没有用的”。meaningless 无意义的，useless 无用的，helpless 无助的，worthless 无价值的。

53. C。本题考查动词。我犯了错，一路上都开车跟着父亲，恳求父亲上车。ask 要求，persuade 劝说，beg 恳求、祈求，follow 跟随。

54. A。本题考查形容词。由父亲采取步行回家的方式可知他还遭受了身体上的痛苦。相对于 emotional（情感上）的是 physical（身体上的），所以选 A。

55. C。本题考查副词。这件事是我最痛苦的经历，也是我最成功的教训。Also 表示“也”，最符合文意。

第二节　语法填空

56. waiting。waiting room 候诊室。

57. other。任何其他症状：any other symptoms。

58. voice。

59. speaking。该句相当于 when I was speaking，前后主语一致，省略掉主语和 be 动词的用法。

60. on。

61. healthy。此处应用形容词。

62. sure。make sure to do sth. 的结构。

63. yearly。形容词修饰“体检”。

64. receptionist。跟前台接待员进行预约，此处应填表示人的名词。

65. shortly。表示“不久以后”，修饰 be with you。

第四部分　写　作

第一节　改写对话

66.

First Two Chinese Astronauts

Recently China sent out another spaceship and there were two astronauts in it. They are Fei Junlong and Nie Haisheng , who are so great and lucky to be sent into the space. It is said that they are chosen from a group of astronauts. The two astronauts are chosen because of their excellent physical and psychological states. Before sent into the space, they were sent to Russia for training to help them get used to the life in the space. After all, they can't sleep or eat in the space like us on the earth. They stayed in the space for more than 115 hours.

第二节　应用文写作

67.

Dear Sir or Madam,

Having read your advertisement in the newspaper, I feel I am qualified for the job.

I'm a 21-year-old boy, 1. 75 meters in height. As a graduate from Beijing Xinhua Travel School, I speak standard Putonghua and excellent English. Interested in Chinese history, geography and culture, I have read a lot about them. So I am familiar with many places of interest. Besides, I worked part-time as a guide for one year when at school.

Given the job, I will make a good guide. My telephone number is 62453348.

Look forward to your early reply.

Yours sincerely,

Li Ming

全真模拟卷(2)

第一部分　听　力

第一节

1. 此题是推断题。由 It's the day before Teacher's Day. 可知选 B。

2. 此题是细节题。由 I forget to tell you that we moved to the Hilton last week. 可知选 C。

3. 此题是细节题。由 I'd like to, but the weather report says it'll snow heavily tomorrow. 可知选 C。

4. 此题是推断题。由 Excuse me, Madam. Can I take Bus 105 to the railway station? 可知选 A。

5. 此题是推断题。由 you have to wait half an hour for our business hours that are from 8:30 am to 5:30 pm. 可知他是 8 点到的,所以选 A。

第二节

6. 此题是推断题。由—What would you like? —I'd like a red wine, please. —Anything else? 可知选 A。

7. 此题是细节题。由 I'll try the Greek salad, please. 可知选 C。

8. 此题是细节题。由 That's 75 cents for the wine and 1.30 for the salad. 可知价格是 $1.3+0.75=2.05$,所以选 C。

9. 此题是推断题。由对话可知两人的身体出现了很多问题,可知他们是老年人,所以选 C。

10. 此题是细节题。可用排除法选出 C。

11. 此题是细节题。由 But I don't do much in the garden now because I've hurt my arm. 可知选 C。

12. 此题是推断题。由 David, you look awful(可怕的). 可知选 B。

13. 此题是细节题。由 I had an accident in the car this morning. 可知选 C。

14. 此题是细节题。由 he must have been coming very fast if you didn't see him. 可知选 C。

15. 此题是细节题。由 She's in conference at the moment. 可知选 C。

16. 此题是推断题。由 Could she phone to confirm that she can come before tomorrow? 可知选 B。

17. 此题是细节题。由—What number is it? —802 9714 Extension 246. 可知选 B。

18. 此题是细节题。由 But as soon as I arrived, I got sick, and could not meet with him. 可知选 C。

19. 此题是推断题。由 I tried to telephone him during office hours, but he was busy. His secretary said that Mr. Smith would call me back, but he didn't. 可知选 C。

20. 此题是推断题。由 I saw a man on the street who looked like Mr. Smith, and I called out to him. It was someone else. 可知选 A。

第二部分　阅　读

第一节　短文理解

21. 选 C。本文围绕 the broken bones 展开。

22. 选 D。根据第一段的 The broken bones of 30 or 40 bodies lay with one on top of the other. 可知。

23. 选 C。根据第二段中的 The queen's servants(仆人) had killed themselves immediately after she had died. 可知。

24. 选 C。由 They work several hours every day, so they can not go to regular school. 可知答案选 C。

25. 选 B。由 Their classes are held in some wonderful places. 可知答案选 B。

26. 选 D。由 They are responsible for making sure … along with their education. 可知答案选 D。

27. 选 C。由 If they do not make much progress in school, they are not permitted to continue working in TV shows. 可知答案选 C。

28. 选 D。从第二段后半段的 However, as Chinese travelers diversified (使多样化) their interests, more and more people decided to travel on their own. 可知。

29. 选 A。倒数第二段的 There are also those, however, who choose to stay where they are. 引出了倒数第一段里另外一部分人的出行方式。

30. 选 B。最后一段的第一句话与选项 A 吻合,第三段与选项 C 吻合,倒数第二段的第一句话语选项 D 吻合。

第二节 补全文章

31. 根据第一句的询问,第一题选 C 表示感谢。

32. Henry 问 Lourie,"明天下午你要干什么",第二题应该是"顺便问一下",选 B。

33. 第三题,Lourie 说"没什么特别的,也许,去拜访一位朋友",选 E。

34. Henry 向 Lourie 发出邀请,第四题选 G。

35. 第五题选 A,表示"太棒了,太好了"。

第三部分 英语知识运用

第一节 完形填空

36. B。本题考查动词短语。give in 屈服、让步; give out 散发、公布; give for 牺牲、交换; give up 放弃。句意: 狮子向外公布消息,他生病即将死去。故选 B。

37. A。本题考查名词。根据后文句意表示即将死亡,故选 A。sick 生病的;glad 开心的;sad 伤心的;dumb 不能说话的。

38. B。本题考查动词。根据上下文句意,狮子要求其他动物来聆听他最后的愿望。listen 不及物动词,后不可直接接宾语;hear 倾听;hear of 听说;learn 学习。故选 B。

39. C。本题考查名词。根据下文内容提示,山羊来到狮子的洞穴。house 房子;hole 洞、孔;cave 洞穴、山洞;shelter 避难所。

40. A。本题考查地点状语。根据上下文可知,山羊来到狮子的洞穴,停留在那里很长时间。故 there 用来修饰 stop 最符合题意。

41. D。本题考查时间副词用法。根据上下文得知,牛是在绵羊之后进洞穴的,而且都是没有出来。故用 before,表示在绵羊出来之前,牛也来到狮子的洞穴。

42. A。本题考查名词辨析。last wishes 遗愿;best wishes 美好的祝愿;good words 好听的话;last word 最终决定。故选 A。

43. B。本题考查连词。and 表并列;but 表转折;so 表如此;although 表尽管。

44. C。本题考查动词。break 打碎、结束; appear 出现; recover 恢复;comfort 舒适、慰藉。根据下文提示,狮子身体恢复,走出洞穴。

45. D。本题考查定语从句连词用法。本句是非限制性定语从句,故用 who。

46. C。本题考查短语辨析。sometime 改天;sometimes 有时;some time 一段时间;some times 几次。根据句意,狐狸在狮子的洞穴外等了一段时间了。故选 C。

47. A。本题考查名词。respects 尊重;admiration 钦佩;honors 荣耀;satisfaction 满足。根据句意,狮子问狐狸为何不去向它表达敬意,故选 A。

48. D。本题考查介词用法。向某人说,用 say to sb。故选 D。

49. C。本题考查动词。beg ... pardon 为固定用法,表示对不起。故选 C。

50. A。本题考查名词。track 踪迹;appearance 出现、露面;way 路;print 印记。

51. B。本题考查名代词。someone 某人;none 没有人;anyone 任何人;nothing 没有什么。根据句意,表示"我发现没有人出来",故选 B。

52. A。本题考查名介词和副词用法。Till 直到……为止;As 当; When 当……时候; After 在……之后。

53. C。本题考查动词短语。like to 喜欢做;want to 想要做;prefer to 宁愿做;have to 不得不做。

54. B。本题考查形容词。worse 更糟糕;easier 更容易;faster 更快;harder 更困难。根据句意表示掉入陷阱更容易,故选 B。

55. A. 本题考查名词。toils 圈套;holes 孔、困境;pits 坑,凹痕;caves 洞穴、山洞。

第二节　语法填空

56. seated。get sb. seated 让某人就座。

57. or。根据句意可以推断出是在 table 或者 booth 之间选择一个,两者选其一,填表示选择的"或者"。

58. few。moments 为复数形式,肯定的语气,之前用 a few 表示一点时间。

59. off。start off,以……作为开始。

60. ready。be ready to do sth. 准备做某事。

61. undecided。根据后半句话的句意,可知顾客还有一点犹豫不决。

62. special。此处用名词形式,表明"特价菜"。

63. personal。个人的喜好,填形容词。

64. dressing。"调料"。

65. with。根据上下文语境可知"一会儿就为您上菜","带着什么东西回来"用 with。

第四部分　写　作

第一节　改写对话

66.

Singapore

Singapore is a very small but modern country. It is called the Diamond Island in the Pacific Ocean. The environment in Singapore is very pleasing. People there are fond of flowers very much and you can see the flowers along the sides of the roads, in the gardens and squares, etc. It's also very clean there because the rules there are very strict. If you smoke in public, you will be fined heavily. So the public order is very good. Besides, people there are very kind and polite. I'd like to pay a visit to Singapore sometime in the future.

第二节　应用文写作

67.

Dear Zhao Na,

I must be leaving for Beijing this evening to deal with something urgent there, so there are the following three things that ought to be done.

1. Please clean our meeting room thoroughly this weekend.

2. Could you please tell all the English teachers to attend the meeting in the meeting room at 3:00p. m. next Monday afternoon?

3. Would you mind taking full notes of the meeting?

I'm sure you can arrange the meeting well and have a successful discussion.

Thanks a lot.

Yours,

Li Ming

全真模拟卷(3)

第一部分　听　力

第一节

1. 此题是推断题。女士说想要一份鸭肉,而男士在回答时使用的称呼是"madam"可知俩人是陌生人,由此可推断选 B。

2. 此题是细节题。女士说 visiting hours are over(探视时间结束了),可知选 A。

3. 此题是细节题。由 weekend, visit a friend of mine, 再根据选项,可知选 C。

4. 此题是推断题。由 I want a single room with a bath,可知对话发生在 hotel, 而女士说 Your room number is 213. It is on the second floor. Here is your key. 可知选 C。

5. 此题是推断题。对话中说 It looks like it's going to snow.(即将要下雪)说明还没下,所以选 C。

第二节

6. 此题是细节题。由 I'm sure we'll have fine weather for our picnic. 可知选 C。

7. 此题是细节题。由对话可知男士邀请女士去野炊,而女士在最后说 Well, I'll go, but I'll take my umbrella with me. 所以选 A。

8. 此题是细节题。由 it's a black leather one with my driver's license, some name cards, and about fifty dollars in it 可知选 B。

9. 此题是推断题。女士丢了钱包,报了警,警察问在哪丢的,她说:I'm pretty sure I had it when I was in the coffee shop. To the shoe department, and then I came here. 可知选 C。

10. 此题是细节题。由女士的回答:I feel a bit tired. That's all. 可知选 C。

11. 此题是推断题。由 Do you remember the new student in my class? 可知女士是一位老师。而男士说 The boy from Haiti? 可知男士对她的班级学生还是有点了解的,而且最后男士还说:It's very kind of you to help them with their studies. 可知选 B。

12. 此题是细节题。由 Do you know any ways of making money? 可知选 A。

13. 此题是细节题。由 How about delivering papers? 可知选 C。

14. 此题是推断题。当男士提出遛狗的工作时,她首先问的是 How much can I make? 当男士说:More than carrying papers. 她立刻就答应了,所以选 B。

15. 此题是细节题。由 The crocodile entered the tent around 4 a. m. on Monday 可知选 A。

16. 此题是细节题。由 luckily a third person shot the crocodile dead just in time, saving the woman 可知选 B。

17. 此题是推断题。根据文章可知,60 岁的老妇人是为了帮助一个 34 岁的年轻人而与鳄鱼搏斗的,根据她的年龄,选 C 更恰当。

18. 此题是细节题。根据 Hello and welcome to the university library. This taped tour will introduce you to our library's facilities(设施)and operating hours. 可知选 A。

19. 此题是推断题。由 Our science and engineering sections can be found on level three. 物理是属于自然科学的,所以选 C。

20. 此题是细节题。由 Graduate students can check out twenty books for four weeks. 可知选 C。

第二部分 阅 读

第一节 短文理解

21. 选 C。从文章第一段的后半部分可知,人们由于各种各样的事物而缩减睡眠的时间。

22. 选 B。文章第三段主要阐述了"睡眠少的人"回忆不起什么来。更有甚者,他们似乎情愿什么都记不住。类似的情况是他们通常处理心理问题的方式:不承认问题的存在,希望只要忙忙碌碌,麻烦总会过去的。因此 B 选项最贴切。

23. 选 B。从倒数第二段和第三段可以排除 A,从最后两段的对比中可以排除 C,从最后一段中可以排除 D。

24. 选 C。本段主要阐述无家可归儿童的数量在不断地上升:"这给已经负担过重的城市教学和教学管理带来了许多额外的麻烦,其中既涉及法律问题又涉及教育问题。"

25. 选 C。本段中有 But the National Coalition for the Homeless estimates that there are at least two times as many homeless children,这是根据本段上文的 there are 220,000 homeless school-age children 而言的。

26. 选 B。本文主要从教育的层面来述及无家可归儿童的，所以选 B。

27. 选 C。原文第一段第二句话 The car is fitted with a remote immobiliser（锁止器），and a radio signal from a control centre miles away will ensure that once the thief switches the engine off, he will not be able to start it again. 表明了答案。

28. 选 B。第三段的内容主要是说现在的车子配有高科技的设备，这使得偷车贼的日子更难过了。因为 The pattern of vehicle crime has changed，只有 B 才符合题意。

29. 选 A。原文第四段第一句话 Modern cars are far tougher to steal, as their engine management computer won't allow them to start unless they receive a unique ID code beamed out by the ignition（点火）key. 先从句子结构角度来分析，这句话的前半句是主句，后半句由 as 引导的部分是原因从句，所以 as 后面的内容就是本题的答案。

30. 选 B。最后一段 Staff at the centre will then contact the owner to confirm that the car really is missing（控制中心的工作人员会和车主确认车子是否确实被偷），与题意相符。选项 A 是在报警前发生的动作，选项 C、D 是在报警后，但都要晚于和车主确认，因此可以排除 A、C、D，正确答案为 B。

第二节　补全文章

31. 询问"Big Apple"这个称呼是什么意思。选 B。

32. 继续询问"Big Apple"这个昵称是怎么来的。选 F。

33. 下文介绍这个昵称的来历，所以第三题应该填一句表示过去发生的事情，E 选项有 1920's。选 E。

34. 第四题的下文提到了 big，G 选项中有 biggest city，符合这句话的意思。选 G。

35. 第五题的后面有"it"，这个词指代的是"New York"，选 C。

第三部分　英语知识运用

第一节　完形填空

36. 选 B。考查动词辨析。killed 被杀；caught 被抓；blamed 被谴责；punished 被处罚。根据下文句意得知，这个年轻人由于偷窃被抓并等待处决。

37. 选 A。考查名词辨析。desire 愿望、渴望；idea 想法；thought 想法；willing 形容词，心甘情愿的。本句意为年轻人表达了想见妈妈的愿望。

38. 选 C。考查动词短语。discuss with 和某人讨论；tell 告诉；speak with 和某人谈话；talk 交谈。从句意看，年轻人想和妈妈交谈，故排除 A 和 B，选 D 则要加介词 with。

39. 选 C。考查时间状语用法。when 当；after 在……之后；before 在……之前；as 当。本句意表示年轻人想在被处决前和妈妈交谈。故选 C。

40. 选 B。考查动词短语形式。句意表达被动，年轻人是被处决。故选 B。

41. 选 A。考查动词短语。come to 来到……面前；come on 要求、开始；come up 提及、靠近，后需接 with 再加宾语；come in 进来，起作用。根据句意，当妈妈走到年轻人面前，年轻人对她说话。

42. 选 D。考查动词辨析。tell 告诉；speak 说；say 说；whisper 低声说、耳语。根据后文，年轻人要求妈妈将耳朵靠近他，故用 whisper 更贴切。

43. 选 C。考查动词短语。take off 脱掉、去除；take away 拿走、解除；bite off 咬掉；get off 离开、出发。根据句意，当妈妈将耳朵靠近年轻人时，他差点把妈妈的耳朵咬了下来。

44. 选 A。考查形容词。horrified 惊恐的，恐惧的；surprised 吃惊的；angry 生气的；indifferent 漠不关心的。根据句意，对于年轻人的行为，旁观者是很惊恐。

45. 选 A。考查疑问词。这里缺少一个名词从句，且关系词在从句中作宾语，故用 what 来引导。

46. 选 B。考查副词。so, such, very, too 都可表达非常。其中 so, very, too 后常常接形容词，而 such 后接名词或名词短语。

47. 选 C。考查动词短语。根据句意，始于做某事，以某事开始，用 begin with doing sth。

48. 选 A。考查介词短语。Instead of 代替、而不是；Despite of 尽管、不管、任凭；Although 尽管；Because

of 因为、由于。根据句意，年轻人诉说，当他偷窃时，妈妈没有斥责、惩罚他，而是笑着对他。故选 A。

49. 选 D。考查动词。cried 哭；was angry 生气；was surprised 吃惊；laughed 笑。根据上下文意，妈妈是笑着对儿子说。故选 D。

50. 选 D。考查动词。look 看；glance 扫视、匆匆一看；see 看；notice 注意。本句中，表示“注意”，用 notice 最贴切。

51. 选 B。根据句意，“因为她，我才有今天。”表示“因为”，且后接名词，用 because of 最准确。

52. 选 A。考查形容词。right 正确的；wrong 错误的；fool 愚蠢的；nonsense 胡说、荒唐。根据下文得知，牧师是认可年轻人的话，他认为年轻人说的对，故选 A。

53. 选 D。考查动词短语。Grow up 成长、长大；Bring up 养育、提到；Pull up 拔起；Train up 训练、培养。

54. 选 A。考查介词短语。in the way 按……方法；on the way 在途中；by the way 顺便；from the way 从……方式。

55. 选 D。考查情态动词。can 可能；might 可能（相较 can，可能性小）；must 一定；should 应该。根据句意，牧师说：“上帝曾经说过，培养一个孩子，他该走的道路；当他老的时候就不会走弯路。”

第二节　语法填空

56. looking。现在完成进行时。

57. to。seem to do 的结构，表示似乎、好像要去做某事。

58. badly。副词修饰动词。

59. sense。make sense 固定搭配，表示“有意义的，合乎情理的”。

60. attractive。形容词形式，表明“有吸引力的”，构成系表结构。

61. out。send out 分发。

62. moving。require doing sth. 的结构。

63. are。who 指代前面的 people，用复数形式。

64. impression。用名词形式。

65. so。I hope so，固定搭配。

第四部分　写　作

第一节　改写对话

66.

Pollution of the Yellow River

Nowadays the pollution of the Yellow River is much more serious than people's imagination. Parts of the river are dry now. Some factories still neglect the environmental rules and throw the waste into the river. Actually they are killing our mother river.

Fortunately, there are some students who are conducting the Mother River Protection Operation. They go to different cities and villages to persuade more and more people to join their movement. To protect the Yellow River, we should also plant more trees along the river and try to make the river clean. If everyone can join the movement, the Yellow River can be saved. After all, our mother river needs everyone's love.

第二节　应用文写作

67.

Dear headmaster,

Having read yesterday's newspaper, I got the news that English teachers are needed in your school. Therefore, I'd like to have a try.

I'm Li Ming, twenty-two years old. I graduated from the English Department of Hunan University in 2005, and ever since then I've been an English teacher in a vocational high school. Besides my good English, I've got many advantages, such as good health, great patience and good relationship with others. What's more, I do think

a male teacher can give children something they can't get from a female teacher. I do hope you will give me a chance. I'll work hard.

Best wishes.

Yours truly,

Li Ming

全真模拟卷(4)

第一部分　听　力

第一节

1. 此题是推断题。由 She wrote many detective books. 可知选 A。

2. 此题是推断题。由 The lecture starts at 8:00. We still have fifteen minutes to go. 可知现在是 7:45,所以选 B。

3. 此题是推断题。由 Listen! The show is starting. Let's hurry up. 可知他们还没进去,所以选 A。

4. 此题是推断题。由 but the beef was a bit well done(有点过火了),可知选 C。

5. 此题是推断题。由 How about taking a ride in the country? 可知选 B。

第二节

6. 此题是细节题。由 Why did you go and tell Mrs. Wallace how much money I am going to make? 可知选 B。

7. 此题是细节题。由 I guess I wasn't thinking. I got all excited. 可知选 C。

8. 此题是推断题。由 They will know in the end. Everyone in this town got a big nose(嗅觉灵敏). 可知选 B。

9. 此题是细节题。由 Please pass me a copy of *China Daily*. (《中国日报》)可知选 C。

10. 此题是推断题。男士说 The Beijing Opera is showing on Saturday evening. Do you like Beijing Opera? 女士说 Let's go and see it, 而地点是在 Beihai Park,可知选 B。

11. 此题是细节题。男士说 The Beijing Opera is showing on Saturday evening. 可知选 B。

12. 此题是推断题。由 I was sick. I had a fever. I couldn't get out of bed. 可知选 B。

13. 此题是推断题。由 He said that I'd be able to take a make-up(补考). 可知选 B。

14. 此题是细节题。由 I didn't think I'd be able to drive today. 可知选 C。

15. 此题是推断题。由 Have you been fired(解雇) by Rogers? 可知选 C。

16. 此题是细节题。由 I told her that I'd just bought a car in my letter. 可知选 C。

17. 此题是细节题。由—But why are you telling her now? —I don't want her to worry about my life here. 可知选 B。

18. 此题是推断题。由 It destroyed the third floor of the building, but fire-fighters saved the first and the second floors. 可知第三层是烧的时间最长的,所以选 C。

19. 此题是细节题。由 The Geller House was built in 1718, 可知选 C。

20. 此题是推断题。由 Five years ago, it was made into a building for the elderly. There were a few elderly people living in the building at the time. 可知选 C。

第二部分　阅　读

第一节　短文理解

21. 选 C。推断题。本文讨论了友谊的重要性。不论是青少年还是老年人,都需要朋友的陪伴。没有人是孤立的,每个人都是社会的一部分,都需要他人的爱、陪伴和关心。文章第二段表明人都需要陪伴和归属感。文章第二段提到没有朋友的青少年和丧偶的老年人常常会有心理问题,并提到陪伴和归属感是他们共同的需求,所以 C 为正确答案。答案 A 和 B 都过于武断,作者只是说一般而言,并没有说一定会,所以不对。

22. 选C。细节题。"No man is an island."(Line 1, Para. 3)的意思是,"没有一个人是孤岛。"暗含的意思是每个人都是社会的一部分。第三段第二句话解释了这句引言的意思:In other words, we are all parts of society,所以C为正确答案。

23. 选C。细节推理题。友谊的亲密程度主要取决于人的个性。见第四段第二句 The degree or intensity of friendship varies depending on the personality of the individuals... 所以C为正确答案。

24. 选C。从第二段第五句话可知。

25. 选C。从第三段最后两句话可知。

26. 选A。从文章的最后一段 By focusing their attention on one object at a time, the men can cross the snow without becoming hopelessly snow-blind or lost. 可知。

27. 选D。从文章的第一段表述中可知。

28. 选B。从第三段的第一句话 Even in the same culture 可以得出第二段主要是讲述不同文化背景。

29. 选C。全文都是围绕体态和感受阐述的。

30. 选C。同上题。

第二节　补全文章

31. 第一题的前文问"你要喝杯咖啡吗?"回答是"我更想喝杯茶,如果你不介意的话。"第一题选B。

32. 第二题根据下文"我去探访了一位朋友",可以判断问的是"你昨天去哪了",选E。

33. 第三题选D,一般疑问句,因为下文是肯定回答。然后接着问"你们谈论了什么?"

34. 第四题回答"我们谈论了语言",选C。

35. 第五题回答的是一个反义疑问句,G选项"没有,我问过",前后矛盾,错误,应该选F。

第三部分　英语知识运用

第一节　完形填空

36. 选B。根据下文得知,本文是以第二人称叙述,故选 yourself。

37. 选C。考查形容词。common 常见的、共同的;ordinary 平凡的、普通的;urgent 紧急的;different 不同的。根据上下文可知,警察接到紧急电话。

38. 选B。根据下文,这位男士一直舞动双臂,发出听不懂的语句,故得知,该男士不会说英文。用"speak no English"。

39. 选A。考查动词短语搭配。pull up 停下、拔起;pull down 拉下、拆毁;pull close 拉近;pull on 用力拉、穿戴。只有 pull up to 表示"追上、赶到",与句意符合。

40. 选C。考查固定短语搭配。"不知道"为"have no idea"。

41. 选A。考查形容词。前文有明确的表示时间的词"one night",所以这里用 dark,表示"黑暗的",更合适。

42. 选D。考查动词。下文有 He just keeps screaming.(他继续尖叫。)故这里用"screaming"较合适。

43. 选A。考查连词。前后句为"他是一名犯罪案件的受害者?或者,他就正在实施犯罪行为?"两句为疑问句,为选择关系,故用A。And 表示并列;But 表示转折;So 表示结果。

44. 选B。考查名词。联系上下文得知,并没有指明何种罪行,故用 crime 较合适。murder 表示谋杀;suicide 表示自杀; killing 表示谋杀、杀戮。

45. 选C。考查动词。下文有"You shout again."(你再次大喊)。故这里用"shout" 较合适。

46. 选C。考查介词与 turn 的搭配。turn in 上缴;turn out 结果是、证明是、出现;turn around 转身;turn up 来到、出现。联系上下文句意,选C。

47. 选D。查动词时态。根据下文的 every night in every major city,故用一般现在时。

48. 选A。考查动词短语搭配。turn out 结果是、证明是、出现;go out 出去、熄灭;get out 离开;become 后不可接任何介词。联系上下文句意,选A。

49. 选C。考查短语搭配。have problem (in) doing sth, 故选C。

50. 选A。考查短语搭配。with the policeman's help 表示“在警察的帮助下”。

51. 选B。考查短语及语态。本句表示“孩子去医院受到照顾、治疗”。被动句,表示“被照顾”,故选B。

52. 选B。考查动词。worked at 表示在……工作;launched 发起、推出;mentioned 提及;joined 加入。结合句意,表示“推出语言服务热线”,故选B。

53. 选D。考查定语从句关系词。本句为非限制性定语从句,指代前面的语言服务热线,只能选which。

54. 选A。考查动词。bridge 动词,缩短差距;move 移动;break 打破;connect 连接、联系。根据上下文句意,表示“消除所有人之间的语言障碍”,故选A。

55. 选C。考查名词。本文通篇叙述由于语言带来的一系列误解等,故这里应为“语言障碍”,选language。psychology 名词,心理;behavior 行为;mental 形容词,心理的。

第二节 语法填空

56. close。根据句意可知,离工作单位很近。

57. to。walk to work, 步行去工作。

58. take。take the bus,乘公交车。

59. long。how long 多长时间。

60. some。some cake 一些蛋糕。

61. cook。厨师。

62. hopeless。形容词,表示“没有希望的,无能的”。

63. cooking。烹饪,烹调。

64. time。have time to do 的结构。

65. different。形容词修饰名词。

第四部分 写 作

第一节 改写对话

66.

Instructions on How to Clean Out the Files

First, prepare some pieces of paper and a very large wastebasket.

Second, all the letters that are kept for more than five years can be thrown away. A few of them may be important, but most of them are just regular mails asking about products or prices.

Third, addresses on the letters should be checked against the computer mailing list. You'd better write down the addresses.

第二节 应用文写作

67.

Dear Sir or Madam,

I'm a student from Experiment High School. I've learned that you want a few part-time English reporters. I'm quite interested in it.

I think I'm qualified for the job. As a student, I've read a lot and have much knowledge in many fields. I'm fond of English and do well in listening, speaking, reading and writing. Besides, it's easy for me to get along well with others. In addition, I once worked as a reporter for my school broadcasting station. So I'm sure I can do the job well if I get the position.

I'm looking forward to hearing from you.

Yours,

Li Ming

全真模拟卷(5)

第一部分 听 力

第一节

1. 此题是细节题。由 the weatherman said it' going to rain this afternoon 可知选 C。

2. 此题是推断题。由 menu 可知选 B。

3. 此题是推断题。由 My father does a lot of business and travels a lot. I like his job. 可知选 A。

4. 此题是推断题。由 W：Will you please take this recorder to my office for me? M：With pleasure. 可知选 A。

5. 此题是推断题。由 I'd like to have it delivered(运送). 可知选 B。

第二节

6. 此题是推断题。由 How are your students doing? 可知女士是位老师。而由 I remember you gave our class a hard final test in my first year of college. Many of us failed. But I really learned a lot from you. 可知男士是女士曾经的学生,由此判断选 A。

7. 此题是细节题。由 I lost my job today. 可知选 B。

8. 此题是推断题。由 Nice to hear from you again after all these years. 可知两人是好久未见的熟识,所以选 B。

9. 此题是推断题。由男士说 You must really enjoy it. 女士回答：Oh, I do. Yeah, it's interesting, 可知选 A。

10. 此题是细节题。由 There are some details I want to discuss with him. 可知选 A。

11. 此题是细节题。由 Dr. Perkins is now at an important meeting. 可知选 C。

12. 此题是细节题。由… they said it would be a good idea to hire a car to get around the city. 可知选 B。

13. 此题是推断题。由 M：How much if I hire a Santana for three days? W：Oh, that will be 1,200 yuan. 可知三天 1200,一天 400,所以选 A。

14. 此题是推断题。由 This is Shanghai Car Rental. 而且男士说 we are just on holiday here for a few days,可知选 A。

15. 此题是推断题。由 I see you bought some duty free items. Were you happy with the prices? 可知选 A。

16. 此题是细节题。由—Were you happy with the prices? —Well, I thought they were a little high. 可知选 C。

17. 此题是推断题。由 How about Immigration? How long did it take you to get through? 可知选 B。

18. 此题是推断题。由 brought to you today by the English Coffee Shop on Montana at Seventh Street in Santa Monica—open twenty-four hours a day with the best food in Santa Monica 可知选 C。

19. 此题是细节题。由 At twelve o'clock, the sun is out after a cloudy morning. 可知选 C。

20. 此题是推断题。由… the temperature is seventy-eight degrees with waves which are two to three feet high. Good waves! 可知选 B。

第二部分 阅 读

第一节 短文理解

21. 选 D。因为他是加拿大人,超过七天的话,750 加元是免税的,因此只需征收 50 加元的部分。

22. 选 A。要根据 48 hours or more 规则:800 美元是免税的,还有 800 美元需要征收 3% 的税。

23. 选 C。对于陆路旅行的话,成人需要护照,不满 15 岁的儿童只需出生证明即可。

24. 选 B。从倒数第二段可知,这是一个涉及多个领域双赢的项目。

25. 选 C。从第九段 But the key issue is really money. 可知,钱是最大的问题。

26. 选 B。从第四段 China has proposed three such projects. 表明了中国有一个大铁路圈的构想。

27. 选 D。细节理解题。根据文中所提到的时间:02/04/2012 - 31/05/2012;01/09/2012 - 31/10/2012;01/06/2012 - 31/08/2012 可知,4 到 10 月活动券有效。故答案为 D。

28. 选 B。细节理解题。根据文中“£ 20 per room, valid(有效的)during stay period of 02/04/2012 - 31/05/2012 and then again 01/09/2012 - 31/10/2012”可知,在 10 月住两个晚上需£ 40。

29. 选 B。细节理解题。根据最后一条规定 The B&Bs reserve the right to refuse voucher holders' bookings for people under the age of 18. 可知答案为 B。

30. 选 A。细节理解题。根据第三条规定 The offer is valid for a basic twin or double room only. 可知。

第二节 补全文章

这个对话是王先生和一名机场工作人员之间发生的,王先生要换机票去东京,并且托运行李。

31. 第一题身为工作人员,为顾客提供服务,询问“能为你做什么?”选 C。

32. 第二题那句话提到航空公司,E 选项有 airline 这个词,选 E。

33. 第三题上文找到新的时间,问王先生是否可以,选 G。

34. 第四题选 D,因为下文王先生说“这是我的行李”。

35. 第五题是对“thank you”的回答,选 A。

第三部分 英语知识运用

第一节 完形填空

36. 选 B。考查形容词短语。be made in 在……制造;be interested in 对……感兴趣;be excited with/about 对……感到兴奋;be astonished at 对……感到惊愕。根据句意,对网络交友感兴趣的人,故选 B。

37. 选 D。考查动词搭配。consider doing sth 考虑做某事。故选 D。

38. 选 B。考查名词。根据下文提示,此处应为 e-mail。

39. 选 A。考查短语。other than 除了(所说事务包含在内);except 除了(不包含在内);more than 超过;despite 尽管、不管。

40. 选 A。考查短语。come across 碰到、遇到;come to 总计、达成;come up 上升、靠近;come out 出现、结果是。

41. 选 C。考查短语。look up 查阅、仰视;check up 校对、检查;set up 建立;stand up 起立。本句为“建立关系”,故选 C。

42. 选 B。考查副词。用 much 来修饰形容词比较级,起强调作用。

43. 选 D。考查动词。hide 隐瞒;include 包含;go 去;reveal 泄露。结合上下文句意,用 reveal 最贴切。

44. 选 C。考查形容词。修饰不可数名词且表示否定,用 little。

45. 选 A。考查短语搭配。very 修饰形容词要置于形容词之前,enough 修饰形容词要置于形容词之后。trustworthy 值得信赖的;worthy 有价值的、配得上的。

46. 选 D。考查形容词。false 假的;true 真实的;another 另一个的; personal 私人的。根据上下文,你认为一个人值得信赖后,就可以把私人邮件地址给他。故选 D。

47. 选 B。考查短语。all in all 总的说来;after all 毕竟;above all 首先、尤其是;in all 总共、共计。

48. 选 C。考查代词。本句表示某个人,故用 someone 较贴切。

49. 选 C。考查短语搭配。give up 放弃;give in 屈服、让步;give out 公布、分发;give on 面对、朝向。

50. 选 A。考查短语。no matter 无论、不管;what matter 这有什么关系;how matter 无此搭配;in matter 关于。

51. 选 A。考查连词。before 在……之前;after 在……之后;when 当; as 当。

52. 选 C。考查关系词。本句为 make sure 的宾语从句,用 that 引导。

53. 选 D。考查形容词。private 私人的;open 开放的、公开的;close 亲近的;public 公众的、公共的。在公共场合,用 public place。

54. 选 B。考查动词搭配。have fun 玩得开心。

55. 选 A。考查形容词。common 常见的、共同的；usual 通常的、惯常的；general 普遍的、全面的；ordinary 平凡的、平淡的。common sense 常识。

第二节　语法填空

56. horrible。此处应填形容词，表示天气很糟糕。

57. raining。continue doing sth 继续做某事。

58. out。come out 出来。

59. inviting。thank sb for sth/doing sth，因某事/做了某事而感谢某人。

60. a。a number of 表示许多。

61. cooking。烹饪，此处应用名词形式。

62. Italian。形容词修饰名词。

63. so。固定搭配。

64. lots。lots of。

65. kidding。开玩笑。

第四部分　写　作

第一节　改写对话

66.

How to Lose Weight

We should lose weight in a healthy way. Some people choose to do more exercise instead of eating less food. Besides, the healthy diet is also very important.

You should eat more vegetables and fruits to get the necessary nutrition. Pay attention to the calories contained in food. For example, the calories in cakes are very high and can make you put on weight easily. But remember calories in white meat are low, which includes chicken, fish, sea food and so on.

第二节　应用文写作

67.

March 15, 2012

Dear Eric,

I came to see you this morning but it was so happened that you were out. So I have to leave this to you.

I'm glad to tell you that after raining so many days, it is said that it will be fine this Sunday. Therefore some of our friends and I have decided to go for an outing. We'll meet at the gate of the Forest Park at 8:30 am. Then we will go climbing and have some games. We'll have a picnic. In the afternoon we'll go boating in the river nearby. If it's possible, we'll go to pick some strawberries. Will you join us? Ring me up before 5:00 pm, please.

Yours,

Li Ming

全真模拟卷(6)

第一部分　听　力

第一节

1. C。推断题。根据对话，男士问可以帮到女士什么；该女士说她有睡眠障碍，凌晨三点醒了就睡不着了。相应交际项目为：看病(Seeing the doctor)。故两者的关系为医生和病人。故选 C。

2. B。计算题。根据对话，该女士从周一到周四每天工作 10 小时，星期五只工作 7 小时，通过计算相加得出她每周工作 47 小时。故选 B。

3. A。推断题。由对话可知，男士引领女士去一张 2 人位的餐桌，女士问男士要餐单看，可推测出男士的职业是餐厅服务员。故选 A。

4. A。细节题。由对话可知,女士想喝一杯加奶但不放糖的咖啡,故选 A。

5. C。理解题。对话中,女士提到只要 follow the directions,就不会有任何问题了。意思是遵照说明来做,故选 C。

第二节

6. B。推断题。由… and has starred in 140 Kung Fu films. 可得知,Mr Rice Guy 是一位演员,故选 B。

7. A。理解题。对话中,男士称 Mr Rice Guy 即便有妻子陪同帮助,也将做饭烧菜上演成一种表演,并详细描述了他精湛的厨艺。故选 A。B、C 选项内容均未提到。

8. B。推断题。由开头的几句对话,可推断出男士将会去伦敦机场迎接与他从未见过面的孙子。

9. B。细节题。由文中 No, that was during the Second World War and I went to Europe on a large warship. 可得知男士二战期间是坐战船去的欧洲。故选 B。

10. A。计算题。由最后一句话可听到现在是下午四点,到达时间是下午六点。通过计算得出说话者两小时后到达目的地。故选 A。

11. A。推断题。根据对话判断该女士是一位滑雪运动员,故选 A。

12. C。细节题。由对话中 I landed the wrong way and fell the rest of the way down. 可得知选 C。

13. C。细节题。对话中 Probably in about two months. 可得知选 C。

14. A。推断题。由… there's no one living over us. 推断出他们的公寓在顶层。故选 A。

15. B。细节题。由对话可以得知选 B。W: Is the place well furnished? M: Yes, it's pretty bright in there and big enough for our children to play.

16. A。推断题。由对话末尾部分可以推断出女士对住处的各种设备较满意,想去房子里再看看。故选 A。

17. A。细节题。由独白中… it is my responsibility to explain the vacation arrangements 听出选项 A。

18. B。细节题。由独白中… have you fill out forms… 选出选项 B。

19. C。推断题。根据 Most college facilities will be closed during the vacation. These facilities include the gymnasium, the college store, and the dining halls. 判断出餐厅关门。或根据 The library and the computer center will be open… 排除 A、B 选项。

20. A。细节题。根据 Only the post office and the college administration offices will be open on regular hours. 选 A。

第二部分 阅 读

第一节 短文理解

21. 选 B。"Inspire a Generation"这句口号激励人,不是奥组委。

22. 选 B。在第三段中提到,英国人认为提及金钱是粗鲁的,特别是问及工资问题。

23. 选 C。passionate 有激情的。

24. 选 B。文章第一段提到 4 月 18 号离伦敦奥运会还有 100 天,推算一下就是 7 月底。

25. 选 D。从文章第一段可以得知答案。

26. 选 B。第三段讲了主要阐述了一门难的课程,老师就会对教学产生焦虑,所以这一段暗指难的科目会影响老师的教学自信。

27. 选 B。从最后一段 This is an interesting study, but the results need to be interpreted as preliminary and in need of replication with a larger sample. 可知。

28. 选 C。第一段和第二段的第一句告诉我们,要在世界范围内观察气候对大自然中生物生命周期的影响,数量有限的科学家不可能足迹遍及天下,为此科学家求助于普通公民的参与。

29. 选 B。第二段第三句中… encourage ordinary people to observe… 的主语是 The citizen scientist movement,即公民参与科学观察的运动。所以 D 不是正确选择。A 和 C 不符合文章的句意,因此也不是正确的选择。这个句子的大意是:这一运动鼓励普通公民根据自己的兴趣爱好进行科学观察,并将观察结果送交数据库，让专门领域的科学家做进一步的观察。

30. 选 A。文章最后一段说，这个计划向所有人开放（open to everyone），所以应选择 A。B,C,D 所述内容都在该段中提到。

第二节　补全文章

31. 第一题问“谁跑了第一名?”下文回答“是 Tom”，所以选 E。

32. 第二题下文说“他跑得非常快”，所以第二题选 C。

33. 第三题选 B，因为下文说“轮到他跳高了”，所以这个空格应该是“让我们去给他加油吧。”

34. 第四题选 G，因为下文说“祝贺你，Bill”。

35. 第五题表示感谢，说“你们的支持也帮了我很多”。选 F。

第三部分　英语知识运用

第一节　完形填空

36. 选 B。考查名词。number 数目；answer 答案；result 结果；question 问题。第二句是第一句的回答，故用 answer。

37. 选 A。考查连词。because 因为；even if 即使；unless 除非；so that 因此。本句意为，他们知道，因为他们就是这样做的。

38. 选 D。考查动词搭配。set into 实施、投入；keep into 无此表达；put into 输入、表达；make into 使……变成……。本句为两个女孩并不想把此变成吉尼斯世界纪录。

39. 选 B。考查动词。understand 理解；help 帮助；please 请；wish 祝愿。本句意为他们只想帮助在飓风中受损失的孩子们。故选 B。

40. 选 C。考查形容词。lost so much 表示损失惨重。故选 C。

41. 选 B。考查动词。write 写；watch 看；hear 听；report 报道。看新闻应为 watch news。

42. 选 A。考查不定代词。none 表示全部否定，没有；some 表示一些；most 表示大部分；all 表示所有，肯定。

43. 选 C。考查动词。get 获得；buy 买；like 想、喜欢；collect 收集。根据句意，“我认为，也许他们想要一个洋娃娃”。故选 C。

44. 选 A。考查动词搭配。share sth with sb 表示和某人分享。

45. 选 B。考查介词短语。by way 经由；under way 在进行中；at way 无此用法；off way 无此用法。

46. 选 C。考查名词。travel 旅行；trip 旅行；plan 计划；study 学习。结合上下文，两个女孩是想实施他们的捐助计划，故选 C。

47. 选 D。考查名词。clothes 衣服；books 书本；money 钱；dolls 洋娃娃。结合上下文，选 D 最贴切。

48. 选 B。考查形容词。strict 严厉的；surprised 惊喜的；angry 生气的；careful 小心的。本句表示两个小女孩对自己的成功感到很惊喜。故选 B。

49. 选 A。考查名词。collection 收集；summer 夏天；school 学校；holiday 假期。根据上文，应为收集时间结束，故选 A。

50. 选 C。考查动词。pay 支付、缴纳；sell 卖；send 寄送；return 返还。根据句意，要把洋娃娃寄送到飓风受灾区的孩子们。故选 C。

51. 选 B。考查疑问词。How feel? 感觉如何?

52. 选 D。考查形容词。interesting 有趣的；friendly 友好的；strange 陌生的、奇怪的；special 特殊的。这里的 friends 是指洋娃娃，所以用 special 较贴切。

53. 选 D。考查名词。hope 希望；smile 微笑；look 看；voice 声音、嗓音、意见。本句表示三人异口同声，故选 D。

54. 选 A。考查形容词。happy 开心的；bad 糟糕的；scared 害怕的；beautiful 美丽的。本句表示这个故事有一个开心圆满的结尾，故选 A。

55. 选 D。考查名词。结合本文第一句,仍用 spare room 表示空房间。

第二节　语法填空

56. over。在过去的几个月里。

57. to。in regard to, 固定搭配。

58. competition。形容词性物主代词后跟名词。

59. advantage。take advantage of 固定搭配,表示“充分利用”。

60. which。引导非限制性定语从句。

61. expanding。think about doing sth, about 是介词,后跟动名词。

62. on。“在什么方面”用介词 on。

63. up。keep up 表示“追上、赶上”。

64. social。此处应该用形容词。

65. technologies。句中出现了 these,后面应该用名词复数形式。

第四部分　写　作

第一节　改写对话

66.

Project Hope

Project Hope is an important measure that our government has taken to help poor children who cannot afford to go to school. The development of education should be a priority in our country. Our country has realized the importance of education. It has taken some good measures on education, such as reducing the students' study costs and increasing the teachers' pay. Our government also encourages young teachers to go to poor areas to help children there.

Furthermore, besides our government, many organizations and people have given plenty of money and school supplies, too. Therefore, many schools have been built and a lot of children get the chance to go to school and get knowledge.

第二节　应用文写作

67.

Dear Mike,

I am very glad to hear that you will come to China. You can live with me in my home. I live in a 6 – story building near Tsinghua University. There is a small park near my home. Once you find the park, you will find my home. It is on the 4th floor.

I live with my parents and my younger sister. My parents both work in a company, and they go to work very early everyday. My sister is an elementary school student.

You can sleep in your spare room during your stay. I think we will have a good time together. And welcome to my home.

Yours,

Li Ming

全真模拟卷(7)

第一部分　听　力

第一节

1. A。推断题。根据对话,女士建议男生找汽修工来及时修车而不是自己修;男士说要请汽修工得先赚足钱,言外之意是找汽修工修车比自己修花钱多。故他自己在修车,选 A。

2. C。推断题。根据对话两人在讨论墙油漆什么颜色,故选 C。

3. B。推断题。女士提醒男士要系安全带,要不然她会觉得紧张,推测出两人在汽车里,故选 B。

4. C。推断题。由女士回答说自己的确有记笔记,但笔记本在朋友那,推断出借给朋友了,选 C。

5. A。细节题。男士问:… Are you trying to sleep? 女士答: Yes, and… 可直接得出答案 A。

第二节

6. C。推断题。由对话开头,男士劝说安慰道:"Don't be so pessimistic; at least you have my friendship."可得知女士很沮丧,选 C。

7. B。细节题。对话中多次提到 Lucy 是 that spoiled rich kid,she was just a rich princess,故选 B。其余两项并未提到。

8. C。推断题。对话中男士最后多次劝说女士先放下身段,主动去修复关系。

9. C。主旨题。对话围绕租车话题,可推测在租车处。

10. A。细节题。由对话:The Hyundai Accent. It's $135.99 per week plus taxes. 可直接得出选 A。

11. B。细节题。由对话—Are you at least 25 with valid driver's license and a valid credit card? —Yes. And yes. 可得出选 B。A、C 两项并未提及。

12. A。主旨题。根据对话可知谈话者在讨论病情,推测出在诊所。故选 A。

13. C。细节题。由对话… We went to an American seafood restaurant… 可以得出选 C。

14. A。主旨题。根据对话者讨论的主要内容可知选 A。

15. B。细节题。由对话中… and the inside lines are for singles. 可得知选 B。

16. C。推断题。由对话 W:… If you get to 40 and win again, you win the game. M:The opponent starts serving then? W:Right. See. You know how to play now. 得知对方是输掉的一方,故选 C。

17. A。主旨题。根据文章的大意可得出各段均围绕噪声污染展开说明。

18. C。语法题。原句是 There is a saying about it being so noisy that you can't hear yourself think. 句中的 so… that … 表示"如此……以至于……";如此喧闹以至于自己听不见自己所想的。故本题选 C。

19. C。细节题。根据 There are two ways to cut down on the harm caused by noise. 可得出选 C。

20. B。推断题。通过把握主旨大意,在末段提出建议,可得知这篇演讲的目的是号召人们行动起来减少噪声污染。

第二部分 阅读

第一节 短文理解

21. 选 A。第四段主要是 Peter Bentley 对飞行机器人的看法。他认为前文描述的进化过程只能使机器人有一些飞行的动作,而要让其起飞则永远不可能,因为不可能有如此大功率的发动机。

22. 选 B。答案在第六段的第三句中。

23. 选 D。文章最后一段具体描述在机器人的进化过程中,指令的进化过程。成功的指令配对后产生新一代的指令,将指令输入机器人,经筛选再进行成功指令配对,再产生新一代指令,如此反复进行。

24. 选 D。第一段第二行提到,在英国足球是很受欢迎的,无论穷人还是富人,年轻人还是老年人。

25. 选 D。第二段提到,英国对足球很重视,把足球最为教育的一部分。

26. 选 A。足球运动是团队运动,不可能使人自私。

27. 选 B。作者的态度是积极的。

28. 选 B。文章主题就是讲教育。

29. 选 D。The more educated a mother is, the more likely are her children—particularly her daughters—to roll and stay in school.

30. 选 D。其他三项文章都有提及。

第二节 补全文章

31. 根据下文"消息走漏得可真快",可以推断第一题是"听说你找到了份工作",选 F。

32. 第二题是对前文 Billy 借钱的回应,"什么时候还? 怎么还?"选 D。

33. 第三题的上文是反义疑问句，要选一个有 Yes 或者 No 的句型来回答，根据对话的意思，"我没有工作，但是我在找"，选 A。

34. 第四题的下文是"那也许比在洛杉矶游荡好"，代词 that 指代的应该是"在他父亲农场工作"，选 C。

35. 第五题下文有 Luck 这个词，所以选择 G，"我所需要的是一点运气"。

第三部分　英语知识运用

第一节　完形填空

36. 选 A。考查动词。begin doing 表示开始做；go on doing 表示继续做；stop doing 表示停止做；continue doing 表示继续做。结合上下文，这里选 A。

37. 选 B。考查副词。quickly 快速地；slowly 慢慢地；soon 不久；at once 立刻。根据上下文，当你又开始利用胳膊和腿的时候，他们又会慢慢变得强壮了。故选 B。

38. 选 C。考查动词。question the fact 表示"质疑这个事实"。

39. 选 A。考查副词。Yet 仍然、已经；Still 已经、还；So 这样、如此；Certainly 当然。结合上下文句意，选 A 更贴切。

40. 选 B。考查动词。seem to know 似乎知道。

41. 选 C。考查形容词。in the same way 以同样的方式。

42. 选 D。考查副词。as 引导时间状语从句，多用于平行结构，表示两个动作同时发生：一个主语同时进行两个动作；一种状态随另一种状态的变化而变化。when 引导时间状语从句，可指时间点，又可指时间段，从句中可用延续性动词，也可用非延续性动词。while 表示"在……的时候"、"在……期间"。它强调主句的动作与从句的动作同时发生或主句的动作发生在从句的动作过程中。while 从句中必须是表示动作或状态的延续性动词。结合上下文，选 D。

43. 选 B。考查词性。修饰动词 mean 只能用副词，再结合句意，只能用 actually。

44. 选 D。考查动词。want 想要；build up 建立；make 制作；keep 保持。结合句意，为"保持记忆力"，故选 D。

45. 选 B。考查副词。again 再一次；else 其他、此外；more 更多的、更大的；once 曾经、一次。根据句意，"其他人"用 someone else 表示。

46. 选 D。考查时态。本段落主要时态为一般现在时，遵循时态一致原则，主语为单数，故选 D。

47. 选 C。考查形容词。poor 贫穷的；weak 虚弱的；strong 强壮的；healthy 健康的。结合上下文，用 strong 比较贴切。

48. 选 C。考查动词。see 看见；hear of 听说；notice 注意到；think of 想到、考虑。结合上下文，用 notice 比较贴切。

49. 选 B。考查副词。结合句意，读写不好的人通常有更好的记忆力，故选 B。

50. 选 C。考查连词。本句是回答上一句的问题，表示"这是因为……"，故选 C。

51. 选 B。考查短语。used to 过去常常；cannot 不能；try to 试图做；have to 不得不。本句意为："这是因为不会读写的人不得不用脑子去记忆。"故选 B。

52. 选 B。考查动词。结合句意"这是因为不会读写的人不得不用脑子去记忆。"故选 B。

53. 选 B。考查动词。根据句意，"他们的记忆就是整个被使用的过程。"being used 动词的分词作后置定语。故选 B。

54. 选 A。考查连词。if 表示如果；that 表示结果；though 表示尽管；thus 表示因此。根据句意"如果你想要有好的记忆力，你就要向这些人学习。"故选 A。

55. 选 C。考查动词。please 请；try 尝试；train 训练；enjoy 享受。根据句意，"你应该通过记住你所想的，所感受到的和所写的来训练（记忆力）。"故选 C。

第二节　语法填空

56. from。从……回来,用 from。

57. have/hold。举行会议:have a meeting/hold a meeting。

58. presentation。make presentation 表示“陈述,表述”。

59. nervous。be 动词后面跟形容词。

60. management。管理阶层,此处应该为名词形式。

61. immediately。副词修饰动词。

62. impressed。该句为被动语态,前面有 be 动词出现,后面的动词用过去分词的形式表示被动。

63. any。根据句意,本句应该为“任何的博物馆”,故而填 any 较为合适。

64. around。take a tour around the town,表示到镇上到处参观旅游。

65. for。thank sb. for doing sth. 表示“因为做了什么事情而感谢某人”。

第四部分　写　作

第一节　改写对话

66.

David's Travel Plan

David has just made plans for the trip to South America during Christmas vacation.

They will fly there since they have booked a honeymoon suite at the Hilton Hotel. They'll have two days to go around that beautiful city. And they can rent a car to tour around. They'll spend the last three days sailing the sea in their houseboat. In the evening they can drink wine and go disco dancing in the ballroom near the hotel. Then they'll go straight to New York by air.

第二节　书面表达

67.

Dear Mr. and Mrs. Green,

I'm writing to you from my home in China. I got back safe and sound. When I think of the wonderful two weeks I spent in Australia, I just can't help thinking of both of you. It was you who provided everything to make my stay such a happy and smooth one. I've learned so much, not only English but also the culture. And I enjoyed a great deal the fun and laughter we shared with each other. Thank you very much. I'll always remember this trip.

I'll keep in touch and write to you later. Please take care!

Yours,

Li Ming

全真模拟卷(8)

第一部分　听　力

第一节

1. C。推断题。根据对话男士要求女士替他将合同打印出来并复印 20 份,可推断两人的关系是老板和秘书,故选 C。

2. C。推断题。根据对话男士想申请银行卡,女士让其出示身份证并填写表格,所以推断对话发生在银行。选 C。

3. B。推断题。根据对话得知男士在 10 点后一小时后才空,故只能选择 10 点以后的时间,选 B。

4. A。推断题。根据对话得知男士不舒服找女士寻求建议,女士建议男士休息并且定时服药,可推断出女士的职业是医生。选 A。

5. A。细节题。I play with a group of guys every Saturday at the park. 男士每周六与一帮朋友打篮球,故选 A。

第二节

6. C。推断题。老师称其星期二和昨天都有迟到,并且有问到前天和昨天迟到的理由是什么,可猜测星期二是前天,故今天是星期四,选 C。

7. B。细节题。对话中可听到 W:Well,I came by taxi yesterday and... M:And you were still late! 故选 B。

8. A。细节题。由 Tuesday I went to see the doctor and I sat in his chair for about two hours. 可得知选 A。

9. B。细节题。由对话中男士说:That mistake could make me lose an important business partner. 可得知选 B。

10. A。细节题。由对话中女士说:I suggest you call them and explain the problem. 可选 A。

11. C。推断题。由开头女士的话语中:I'm afraid it was just a mistake. He is new here,you see. 可以推断出犯错误的那个人是新手。跟 C 选项中的"green hand"意思一样。

12. A。主旨题。根据对话内容判断出两者是在讨论新年心愿。

13. B。细节题。根据 M:Hmm, I stopped smoking last June. That was last year's promise to myself. 推断出选 B。

14. C。细节题。根据女士说:Jeff told me he'd like to have a really nice vacation. 推断选 C。

15. A。推断题。男士说: This morning,I wanted to have some noodles so I boiled some hot water ... 推测出男士早晨吃的是面条。选 A。

16. C。细节题。男士说:I tried to get out of the way and hit my head against a window. 故选 C。

17. B。细节题。男士转述:The doctor told me to keep my arm clean and dry... 故选 B。

18. C。推断题。独白中约翰四年前进入高中,那时候 16 岁,故现在 20 岁,后又提到:He even won a silver medal in the 800-meter race at the school sports meeting a year ago. 故现在 19 岁,选 C。

19. B。推断题。从父母奖励电脑给约翰之后,一切开始改变。学习兴趣下降,加上熬夜随之而来。故选 B。

20. A。推断题。由最后的一句话:He was rather glad to know that his mother cared about him so much. 推断选 A。

第二部分 阅 读

第一节 短文理解

21. 选 B。本文讲述的就是糖的历史。

22. 选 D。以前糖 90% 用于食物,以后将更大范围地用于其他领域。

23. 选 B。文章第一句话就有提及。

24. 选 D。犯罪是个普遍现象,所以 D 表述不正确。

25. 选 A。理解题,词组意思是"逃税"。

26. 选 B。第一段最后 Whatever you do, wherever you go, you are a victim of crime whether you like it or not, whether you know it or not. 所以选 B,即使跟犯罪没有直接联系还是会受到牵连。

27. 选 C。Crime, especially violent crime, has risen to a point where many people are afraid to walk alone in their own neighborhoods, afraid to open their door after dark. 说明暴力行为是最为严重的。

28. 选 D。从第一段 In fact, eyestrain surpasses even wrist pain as the top physical complaint among heavy computer users. 可以得知。

29. 选 D。从第四段 But those liquid crystal display (LCD) monitors, like those found on laptop computers, are easier on the eyes because they display sharper images. 可知。

30. 选 D。最后一段 This is especially a problem for contact-lenses wearers.

第二节 补全文章

31. 根据上文,他会戒烟,第一题选 G,"我想这次他会尽力戒烟的"。

32. 第二题下文是“我什么都做不了”,所以选 C,“我已经尽力了”。

33. 第三题选 B,因为下文说“他看上去气色不好”。

34. 第四题选 F,“他夜以继日地写书”,下文说“今天早上都没剃须”。

35. 第五题选 E,根据上文,“我要和院长谈谈关于他的情况”,第五个空格“是的,或许院长能给他放几天假”。

第三部分 英语知识运用

第一节 完形填空

36. 选 C。考查动词。contact 接触、联系;contract 合同;communicate 交流;connect 连接。根据句意,“动物们互相交流”,故选 C。

37. 选 B。考查形容词。根据下文句意得知,“动物们是以不同的方式交流”,故选 B。

38. 选 C。考查动词。根据句意,“蚂蚁利用气味来告知其他蚂蚁”,“利用什么做什么”表达为 use sth to do sth。故选 C。

39. 选 A。考查动词。do a dance 表示跳一个舞,习惯性搭配。故选 A。

40. 选 D。考查名词。situation 形势、局面、处境;condition 条件、情况;environment 环境;location 位置、地点。根据句意,“蜜蜂通过跳舞来告知其他蜜蜂花儿的位置。”故选 D。

41. 选 A。考查动词。exchange 交换;change 改变;pass 通过、传递;deliver 递送、交付。根据句意,exchange information 交换信息。

42. 选 D。考查名词。根据句意,“大象和鲸鱼是通过声音来交换信息。”故选 D。

43. 选 A。考查形容词。certain 确定的,某个;sure 肯定的、可靠的;kind 善良的;definite 明确的、一定的。结合句意,a certain whale 表示某条鲸鱼。

44. 选 B。考查动词。结合上下文,鲸鱼是通过声音来传递信息,所以本句用 hear 较贴切。

45. 选 B。考查名词。结合上下文,人类是用语言(来交流)。

46. 选 A。考查动词。wonder 想知道;wander 闲逛、徘徊;wonderful 形容词,精彩的、极好的;suspect 怀疑、猜想。根据句意,许多人想知道,动物也会使用语言吗?故选 A。

47. 选 C。考查介词。在多少世纪多少年代前用介词 in。

48. 选 D。考查动词。learn 学习;show 展示;give 给予;teach 教授。根据句意,两位老师向猩猩教授 ASL。故选 D。

49. 选 A。考查动词。根据句意,他们给猩猩取名为 Washoe。故选 A。

50. 选 B。考查介词。根据句意,到 5 岁时,猩猩 Washoe 认识并会使用超过 160 个标识。故选 B。

51. 选 C。考查名词。结合上下文,猩猩 Washoe 可以利用她所学的词汇与人类交流,还可以与其他动物交流。故选 C。

52. 选 A。考查动词短语。sign to 对……做手势;say to 对……说;talk with 和……聊天;call 打电话。根据句意,猩猩 Washoe 是不会说话的,故只能用 sign to herself,表示跟自己打招呼,做手势。

53. 选 C。考查形容词。another 另一个、再一个;other 其他的、另外的;the other 另一个;most 大部分的。根据句意,猩猩 Washoe 和其他的猩猩,这个猩猩是确指的,故用 the other 更符合。

54. 选 C。考查动词。form 形成;invent 发明;make 制作;discover 发现。make a word 造字,固定用法,故选 C。

55. 选 A。考查时态。结合上下文,这里仍然用过去时态,Metal hot 看作一个整体,是一个词,单数,故选用 was。

第二节 语法填空

56. ringing。hear sb/sth doing sth 听到……正在做什么。

57. on。work on 从事,致力于。

58. that/which/不填。本句为定语从句,关系代词可以选择多种答案。

59. representatives。根据句意,我早上见了"代表",此处应该填名词形式,表示人。

60. from。来自于……(地方的)代表们。

61. Sounds。听起来怎么样。

62. boring。形容词修饰名词,物体或事情用-ing 形式。

63. with。agree with sb 同意某人的观点。

64. about。tell sb about sth 告诉某人关于某事。

65. What。固定句型结构,"你认为……怎么样"。

第四部分 写 作

第一节 改写对话

66.

Why Should We Stop Smoking?

Nowadays everyone is in a hurry to do all kinds of things in the society. To ease their pressure, some people choose cigarettes to relax themselves.

However, we should choose other ways instead of smoking because smoking is a really bad habit. Many people suffer from disease because of smoking. And people who smoke should realize that not only themselves but also the people around them are all damaged by nicotine. Since it is very hard for smokers to quit the bad habit soon, they can try to give up cigarettes gradually.

第二节 应用文写作

67.

Dear Sir or Madam,

It is our pleasure to inform you that the International Meeting on City Planning will be held from the 12th to the 14th of October in the Conference Hall of the Beijing People's Building. The meeting will begin at 9 am on the 12th and end at 5 pm on the 14th. A formal dinner in honor of all the guests will be held on the evening of the first day of the meeting. To get to the city from the airport, there are buses that leave every half hour. You may also take the taxi. You will be staying at Beijing Hotel and Jianguomen Hotel. Would you please contact us after checking in at your hotel. Our phone number is 70554323.

Many thanks.

Li Ming

Secretary

Office of International Meeting on City Planning

全真模拟卷(9)

第一部分 听 力

第一节

1. B。细节题。由最后一句话可以知道 Linda 在教室,故选 B。

2. A。细节题。由对话… and I'd like to see my parents first. 可知选 A。

3. C。推断题。由该句 And now I've got to write the paper based on the information I've collected. 推断选 C。

4. C。细节题。由该句 Tom said he could get your club some tickets to the game if you're interested. 得知选 C。

5. C。语法题。Why not? 的言外之意即赞同说话人的意见。

第二节

6. B。推断题。由对话得知说话两人在讨论开张事宜及贴标语。故推断两人的关系是工作关系,选 B。

7. A。主旨题。对话可得知,说话者意图想开连锁店,并且希望该店最终满足顾客需求。

8. C。细节题。根据女士的话语推断出该题选 C。W: I ordered breakfast from room service. Oh, at least half an hour ago.

9. A。细节题。对话开头即点明了说话人的身份。W: Can't you do something about the service in the hotel, manager? 故选 A。

10. C。推断题。由女士抱怨 I've telephoned room service three times, but my breakfast still hasn't come. 反映出女士对此不满,故选 C。

11. A。细节题。由女士说:... But most of us work in pet hospitals. 可选 A。

12. C。推断题。根据女士的话:We run blood and other tests, give shorts and prepare medicine. 可推断出答案 C。

13. C。推断题。由对话最后一句推断出女士的工作对他们帮助很大。故选 C。

14. B。主旨题。由对话大意可以分析出说话人在讨论旅行计划。

15. A。细节题。由女士的话语中: I have been reading weather reports for the Caibbean on the Internet. 可以分析得出女士关注天气预报。

16. B。细节题。由男士话语:... And the islands had been hit by storms two weeks before. 可以选出 B 选项。A、C 并未提及。

17. A。细节题。开头直接点出作者十年前的工作,故选 A。

18. A。推断题。这篇文章开篇就提到下面说说"我的生活"并用第一人称来说话,并未出现其他主人公,故推断选 A。

19. B。理解题。由原文 I had everything that I thought I wanted. But going into work every day took away a bit of myself. 理解其意思为:以为得到了自己想要的,其实却不是很喜欢。故选 B。

20. C。推断题。由文中最后两句 If I hadn't made that choice to take a chance to do something that really thrilled me, I don't think I could have lived with myself. 以及说话人的语气推断出她对现在很满意。

第二部分 阅 读

第一节 短文理解

21. 选 D。第四段有提到 In 1914, President Woodrow Wilson officially proclaimed Mother's Day as a national holiday to be held on the second Sunday of May.

22. 选 A。第二段有提到 Howe, who wrote the words to the Battle Hymn of the Republic, saw Mother's Day as being dedicated to peace.

23. 选 C。第三段有提到... her mother, who died in 1905 and who had, in the late 19th century, tried to establish "Mother's Friendship Days" as a way to heal the scars of the Civil War.

24. 选 C。"Over"是"超过"的意思,精神超过物质,那就说明精神更重要。

25. 选 C。第二段有提及 The mind and the body are integrated system.

26. 选 D。第三段 The brain's neuro-chemistry programs a person to react in one of the classic ways: fight, flight or fright. 理解一下没有提及 D 选项。

27. 选 D。全篇没有提及需要看医生。

28. 选 D。这个故事充满了神话色彩,所以选 D,希腊神话。

29. 选 A。文章第一段就阐述了那西塞斯的自恋情结。

30. 选 A。推断题,现在水仙花就是生长在水里的一种花。

第二节 补全文章

31. 根据下文,医生的意见是"吃得太多",选 C。

32. "我不明白,你是什么意思?"选 F。

33.“你的意思是我太胖了？那就是问题所在，如果我想变瘦一点我该做什么？”选 D。

34. 下文的意思是“如果你想变得更瘦更健康，就要少吃点，多做运动”。选 G。

35. 对于医生的建议，表示感谢和没问题，选 E。

第三部分　英语知识运用

第一节　完形填空

36. 选 B。考查名词。well-being 为固定用法，表示康乐、安宁。故只能选 B。

37. 选 A。考查介词短语。according to 根据；depend on 依赖、取决于；because of 由于；as 因为。根据上下文句意，“据研究表明”，故选 A。

38. 选 B。考查介词。in 和 at 都可表示地点，而 in 表示的地点比 at 所表示的地点大。本句具体到某个大学，故选 B。

39. 选 C。考查副词。Even if 表示即使；Even though 也表示即使；Even 表示甚至；Although 表示尽管。根据句意，此处表示“甚至一些人”，故选 C。

40. 选 D。考查短语。a little 与 little 用来形容不可数名词。few 与 a few 修饰不可数名词。a few 表示肯定，few 表示否定。根据上下文，此处选 D。

41. 选 C。考查短语搭配。根据前文有 more depression 为比较级，故用 than。

42. 选 B。考查数词。数词常与名词连用构成复合定语，中间要用连字符，而且只用名词的单数形式。故本句表示“两年的研究显示”，只能用 two-year study showed。

43. 选 A。考查连词。that 引导名词从句；because 与 for 后接原因状语从句；as 可引导时间、原因、方式状语从句。本句中 but 为并列连词，前后的句子结构应该相一致，故此处选用 that，与后文的 but that using 对应。

44. 选 C。考查形容词。surprising 令人惊讶的；astonishing 惊人的；surprised 吃惊的；frightened 受到惊吓的。根据本句意，“对……感到吃惊”用短语 be surprised at sth。

45. 选 B。考查定语从句关系词的选用。本句为非限制性定语从句，所修饰的先行词为 result，故此处只能用 which。

46. 选 A。考查形容词。contrary 相反的，用法为 be contrary to；contrastive 对比的；different 不同的，用法为 be different from；same 一样的，用法为 the same as。根据句意，此处选 A。

47. 选 A。考查形容词。根据句意，后接 than，此处应用比较级，healthy 的比较级为 healthier。

48. 选 D。考查连词。本句中，the fact 后接同位语从句，故用 that 连接。

49. 选 C。考查动词。count 表示“计算”或“依赖”，作“依赖”时，后接 on；explain 解释，用法为 explain sth to sb；account 作“解释”讲时，后接 for；indicate 指示、象征，为及物动词。

50. 选 A。考查形容词。actual 实际的、事实上的；imaginable 可想象的；magic 是名词，表示“魔术、魔法”；ideal 理想的、完美的。本句意为，和面对面的实际上的交谈相比，这种见不着面、看不见人的“虚”的交流可能会使人从心理上缺乏满足感。

51. 选 C。考查动词。本句中用 formed 动词的过去分词作后置定语，表示“通过这种形式形成的关系往往比较淡”。

52. 选 B。考查形容词。根据上下文句意，表示“通过这种形式形成的关系往往比较淡”。“淡、浅”此处用 lighter 比较合适。

53. 选 D。考查副词。根据句意，“这和如何使用有关”，故选用 how。

54. 选 A。考查介词。point in 在……有用；point at 指出；point to 指向、意味着。根据句意，此处选 A。

55. 选 A。考查名词。in terms of 为固定用法，意为“就……而言，在……方面”。故只能选 A。

第二节　语法填空

56. concerned。be concerned about 关心，关注。

57. on。on schedule。

58. Unfortunately。"不幸的是"。

59. troublesome。前面有 be 动词出现,此处应填形容词。

60. excuses。"理由,借口",复数形式。

61. back。cut back 根据句意,表示"削减,砍掉"。

62. deliveries。"投递"。

63. distribution。名词修饰名词,表示"分发,分配"。

64. services。deliveries services,表示"投递服务"。

65. urgent。此处应填形容词,表示"紧急的"。

第四部分　写　作

第一节　改写对话

66.

Global Positioning System

The Global Positioning System is used for locating things. It operates through the use of 24 satellites that are circling the earth. The satellites send over their location and time 1,000 times a second. The computer on earth receives this information from several satellites and with that information it will find your exact position.

The Global Positioning System was first used by an engineer whose car stopped in a parking place. His call for help was received by a safety department. And within minutes a truck was there for help. By now system has been used successfully in wartime too, during the Gulf War and the Iraq War.

第二节　应用文写作

67.

Dear manager,

I am a student of Beijing University. Here I write to complain an unpleasant experience in your bookstore, Yesterday I bought a Chinese-English dictionary in your bookstore. During my first time using it, I found that several pages had already been broken. So I went back to the bookstore to have it changed. To my surprise, the shop assistant refused to change it for me. When I mentioned the broken pages, he insisted that I had torn them. They had no patience to hear my explanation.

Of course, I had to come back with the broken dictionary. Therefore, I write to you hoping that you can make them improve their service quality.

Thank you for your concerns.

Yours,

Li Ming

全真模拟卷(10)

第一部分　听　力

第一节

1. A。推断题。通过句型 I think we should... 判断出是在提建议。故选 A。

2. B。计算题。通过对话限速 55 英里每小时,到说话人提到现在超过了 15 英里每小时,相加可以得到现在 70 英里每小时的速度,故选 B。

3. B。推断题。通过对话可得出女士正在试夹克衫。故选 B。

4. C。推断题。除了说话者男女两人还提到了 Barbara 和 Charles,故是 4 人,选 C。

5. B。理解题。由男士回答 It doesn't matter. 可见男士并不是很介意吃什么。

第二节

6. A。推断题。由对话内容推断对话发生在酒店,这位女士负责给房间钥匙,故选 A,酒店工作人员。

7. A。细节题。由男士的话:I will need a meeting room tomorrow. Do you have one in the hotel? 得知男士因为要开会来订房间。故选 A。

8. C。推断题。由男士说:Could you break a 20 for me? 推断他想换 20 元零钱,故选 C。

9. A。推断题。男士要求要 2 张 5 元的,问售货员有没有,售货员说有,但没有足够的 1 元的,故选 A。

10. A。推断题。两人一直在讨论换零钱的事宜。故两人的关系可推断是售货员和顾客。选 A。

11. B。推断题。由 W: I grew up in west London. 推断出是在英国长大。故选 B。

12. B。细节题。由 So you see, in one country, you can experience different customs from three different societies. That is something special about Singapore. 可推断出 B。

13. C。细节题。直接有提到的句子是:... so I got quite a lot of people looking at me, which was quite annoying. 故选 C。

14. A。细节题。由男士的话语直接判定:I am just staying here for two months while my friends are out of the city. 他住在朋友家。故选 A。

15. C。细节题。由 Afterwards I stopped at a café for a drink and I got back here just after 11 o'clock. 直接得到答案 C。

16. C。细节题。这句话 I know my friends will be especially sad about the paintings. 点明题意。故选 C。

17. B。推断题。由女士问话的内容和口气可以判定女士有可能是警察。诸如,"准确说,你如何发现家里被盗?""你如何那么确定是在那个时间?"等。故选 B。

18. C。细节题。由独白中:Chinese is spoken by more people than any other language。可以得知该题选 C。

19. B。细节题。由 Today Esperanto is still spoken by eight million people around the world, and it is a language accepted by the Post Office. 可选出 B。

20. A。细节题。One of them was Dr. Zamenhof—a Polish word expert. In 1887, he introduced Esperanto. 直接点出答案选 A。

第二部分 阅 读

第一节 短文理解

21. 选 C。推理题。文中提到是 15 年前的一件事,当时他 8 岁,所以现在是 23 岁。

22. 选 C。因为是那个妇女打翻了鸡蛋箱子,所以要受到指责的是那个妇女。

23. 选 A。A 选项显然不正确,妇女打翻鸡蛋箱子后并没有受到经理的指责。

24. 选 A。第二段 The modern version is usually made of tissue-paper rather than the traditional silk. 说明古代是用丝绸做风筝的。

25. 选 C。文章第三段, German U-boats flew kites from their towers to lift people into the air to watch the land. These kites, which are no longer in existence, were made of light-weight cloth. 可以找到答案 C。

26. 选 B。Man-lifting kites were developed in ancient times, again by the Chinese, for getting information from walled cities and army camps.

27. 选 D。第二段 Why are men and women willing to suffer cold and hardship, and to take risks on high mountains? A、B、C 都有提及。

28. 选 B。第三段有提到 Mountaineering is a sport and not a game. There are no man-made rules, as there are for such games as golf and football.

29. 选 A。第五段有提到 The mountain climber knows that he may have to fight forces that are stronger and more powerful than man. He has to fight the forces of nature.

30. 选 C。最合适的题目是登山。

第二节 补全文章

31. 根据 $175 一周的提示,第一题应该是问薪水,选 F。

32. 选 D,这个孩子觉得这个工作听起来不太有趣。他父亲建议他尝试这份工作。

33. 选 G,"我也许可以找到一个更好的工作。"

34. 选 C,"我建议你接受它,然后再换工作如果你不喜欢。"

35. 根据下文"我会好好考虑一下",选 A。

第三部分 英语知识运用

第一节 完形填空

36. B。本题考查形容词。从本句的 always had something positive to say 可知,Jerry 是个积极乐观的人,所以经常情绪很好。

37. D。本题考查副词。从第 37 空下一句 The reason the waiters liked to follow Jerry very much was 中的 very much 可知 Jerry 应该是"经常"被这样的几个人跟随着。

38. C。本题考查名词。从后面的 motivator 可知,这些服务员跟随 Jerry 的主要原因是乐观的态度很激励人。

39. D。本题考查连词,结合上下文可知,此处开始讲具体的情况,用 if 表示条件。

40. A。本题考查动词。Tell 有"告诉"的意思。根据上下文可知,当员工情绪不好的时候,Jerry 会告诉他们如何看待事情好的一面。B、C、D 不符合文意。

41. B。本题考查形容词。由本空后面的作者对 Jerry 的询问可以判断,作者对 Jerry 的做事风格感到好奇。curious 好奇的,ashamed 羞愧的,excited 激动的,crazy 疯狂的。

42. A。本题考查动词短语。我因为感到好奇,所以就去找 Jerry 了。只有 A 符合文意,go up to 有"去"的意思。

43. D。本题考查动词。这里是说:我真是不明白,你不可能一直都是乐观的。你怎么做到这点的呢? get 有"理解、明白"的意思,符合上下文。

44. C。本题考查名词。由该空后一句话可知,是指两种"选择",故选 C。

45. B。本题考查副词。根据上下文可知,or 连接了两种截然不同的情况,or 后面说的是你可以选择态度消极,因此要填入的部分是关于"积极的"生活态度,因此选项 B 符合题意。

46. D。本题考查动词短语。Jerry 是个乐观的人,所以会从不好的事情当中"吸取教训",learn from 有"从……吸取教训"的意思。

47. C。本题考查形容词。positive 可表示"肯定的,积极的"。结合上下文可知 Jerry 是个乐观的人,总是看生活中积极的一面,由本空的后一句话可知答案选 C。

48. B。本题考查动词。由上下文可知,此处应是"同意"上面所说的话。

49. B。本题考查名词。结合上下文可知 Jerry 是在谈论生活的态度。

50. D。本题考查动词。这里是说:你自己选择如何对待各种情况。react to 是"对……做出反应"的意思,treat 表示"对待"时是及物动词,后面直接加宾语,没有 to。故选 D。

51. A。本题考查动词。affect 影响;exchange 交换;inspire 鼓舞;feel 感觉。根据上下文可知这里是说:你自己选择人们如何"影响"你的情绪,只有 affect 符合本意。

52. C。本题考查副词。这里是说:"如何"生活是你自己的选择。C 符合上下文。

53. B。本题考查名词。Start one's own business 指"自己创业",符合上下文。

54. A。本题考查动词。根据上下文可知,我自己创业后,逐渐和 Jerry 失去了联系。lose touch 可表示"失去联系"。

55. D。本题考查介词短语。该句意思是:当我在生活中做选择时总会想起 Jerry"而不是"怨天尤人。instead of"而不是",后面可加动名词形式。其他三项不合题意。

第二节 语法填空

56. on。on a date 表示"约会"。

57. to。sit down next to sb"坐在什么人边上"用 next to。

58. confident。be 动词后面用形容词,构成系表结构。
59. dangerous。be 动词后面用形容词,构成系表结构。
60. about。be crazy about, 对……着迷的。
61. joking。开玩笑。
62. over。over there 那儿,go over there 表示"去那儿"。
63. yourself。introduce oneself 做自我介绍,用反身代词。
64. easy。as ... as ... 中间应该用形容词或者副词的原级来做比较。
65. luck。good luck 表示"祝你好运"。

第四部分 写 作

第一节 改写对话

66.

The London Subway

The London Subway is less clean and bright than that in Beijing. But there are much more subway stations in London. Thus the subway system in London is rather convenient. You can get almost anywhere rather quickly on a subway, especially when the traffic is heavy. All of the stations are equipped with automated vending machines, which are extremely convenient, allowing you to buy tickets whenever you want. Besides, some subway train even provide smoking cars for smokers.

第二节 应用文写作

67.

Dear John,

I have decided to write to you in English—It's good practice for both of us!

I've been in the Northeast University for two months. I'm living on campus in a student dorm together with two other classmates. The campus is ten miles away from downtown, so I haven't been out of the campus much. The campus has its own shops, post office and banks. The library provides all kinds of books. Life is convenient here.

As for students, we seem to have so much to read—it's never-ending. On the other hand, we don't seem to have any exams. What we do have are essays. I've got three all due in next week. So be prepared for lots of reading and writing if you want to study here. School life is busy, but interesting.

Li Ming

听力录音材料

全真模拟卷(1)

M：Excuse me. Can you tell me how much the shirt is?

W：Yes, it's nine fifteen.

Text 1

M：Would you rather live in big cities or in the country?

W：I'd rather not live in big cities.

Text 2

M：I'm terribly sorry, I've broken a glass.

W：Oh, that doesn't matter.

M：I'm sorry. Tell me where you bought it, so I can get you another.

Text 3

W：Bill, that is a lovely painting in your living-room.

M：I'm glad you like it. It's a Christmas gift from my son.

W：Well, it's beautiful. Your son has very good taste.

Text 4

M：So how is your new roommate?

W：She really makes me angry.

M：What happened?

W：She's always making loud noises at midnight. When I remind her, she's always rude.

Text 5

W：Excuse me, I'm looking for Mr. Tang.

M：Oh, he is not on this floor. He is on the fourth floor. Go down the stairs and turn left.

Text 6

M：Did you finish typing that report?

W：Yes, I did, but I worked late.

M：But it must be a long report, I guess.

W：Exactly. Twelve pages. I spent three hours on it.

M：By the way, what time did you go home?

W：I left the office at nine o'clock. I got home at ten.

M：What did you have for dinner?

W：I sent out for a sandwich and ate at my desk.

Text 7

M：Fikky, what's going on? Freggis just told me that you're going to be leaving us.

W：Yes, I really feel bad out of it. But B. N. D. came up with really good offer.

M：Well, I didn't know you were going to look for a new job.

W: Well, just between you and me. I think we have some real problems in this department. Don't get me wrong. It has nothing to do with you, Frank. Everybody says you are an excellent manager.

M: Problems, what problems? Do we have time to talk about it?

Text 8

W: You know I just finished some very interesting research for the newspaper about things people do in their spare time.

M: Really? What did you learn?

W: Well, I talked to 20 people and 19 of them watch TV.

M: That's interesting. I never watch it, do you?

W: Not much. Anyway, about half of them, 9 people, play some kind of sport.

M: I'm not surprised. People are getting more exercise these days.

W: Yes, a few of them go to movies.

M: Mm, I do, too.

W: But here is the most interesting result: only one of them reads.

M: That's terrible.

Text 9

M: Excuse me, do you mind if I sit here?

W: No, not at all. Go ahead.

M: Thank you.

W: Are you going somewhere or meeting someone?

M: I am on my way to Washington. And you?

W: I am on my way to San Francisco.

M: Really? I think San Francisco is probably the most exciting city in the US.

W: So do I. No other city has as many good restaurants or as much good music.

M: Is San Francisco your hometown?

W: I am from a very small town in Pennsylvania. I wouldn't want to live there again, either. I don't like to live in a small town very much.

M: Neither do I. But small towns have their advantages: less traffic—

W: And friendlier people. You know, I'm beginning to feel homesick. By the way, where are you from?

M: China.

W: China? But you speak English like a native speaker. I didn't have any idea.

M: Oh, excuse me. It's time for my flight. Well, it's been nice talking with you.

W: You, too. Bye!

Text 10

M: Could you suggest some ways to bring family members closer together?

W: Well, I feel it is very important for families to have regular meals together. One of my good childhood memories was dinner with my parents and two sisters. Because my husband and I both worked and our three children were busy with their studies, we seldom had a chance to get together as a family. But we thought it would be possible for us to sit down and enjoy meals together every week. First we tried setting fixed days: Mondays, Wednesdays, and Fridays. But almost everyone was unhappy. Then my son had the idea that everyone told his or her most convenient days and I would choose the two best days. For a while the children were still unhappy with the idea. They said they would rather spend the time with their friends playing sports. Gradually, though, they began to see the evenings together as interesting and helpful. We loved a lot. We made plans for trips. We discussed each other's problems. After a couple of months anyone who had to miss a family meal felt regretful. And now we all feel that we have been able to build stronger relationships within the family than we had before.

全真模拟卷(2)

M: Excuse me. Can you tell me how much the shirt is?

W: Yes, it's nine fifteen.

Text 1

W: Paul, do you remember Jessica's birthday?

M: Yeah. It's the day before Teacher's Day.

Text 2

M: Jane, do you still live in the China Great Hotel?

W: Oh, I forget to tell you that we moved to the Hilton last week.

Text 3

M: Helen, I am going to take my son to the zoo tomorrow morning. Would you like to go with us?

W: I'd like to, but the weather report says it'll snow heavily tomorrow.

Text 4

M: Excuse me, Madam. Can I take Bus 105 to the railway station?

W: Sorry, I am also new here. Maybe you can ask someone else.

Text 5

W: Sir, can I come in now?

M: Sorry, Lady. I am afraid that you have to wait half an hour for our business hours that are from 8:30 am to 5:30 pm.

Text 6

W: Good morning, Sir. What would you like?

M: I'd like a red wine, please.

W: Anything else?

M: What snacks have you got?

W: The menu is on the board over there. There's pancake, Greek salad, steak and chips...

M: I'll try the Greek salad, please. Do I pay now?

W: Oh, yes, if you would. That's 75 cents for the wine and 1.30 for the salad.

Text 7

M: Hello. How are you today?

W: Not so good. My leg's playing me up, awful pains in my leg and my toothache!

M: Oh, dear! I've got toothache too and the dentist says he simply can't see me before next week. But what gets me is my headache.

W: I know what you mean, but at least you can do the garden. I can't even do that with my back, the doctor says I mustn't lift or bend.

M: You poor thing. There's nothing worse than back trouble. But I don't do much in the garden now because I've hurt my arm. It's really painful.

W: Like my ankle. It's all swollen up.

Text 8

W: Hi, David, you look awful. What's the trouble?

M: Well, believe it or not, I had an accident in the car this morning. Someone drove into the back of my car.

W: No! How did it happen?

M: I was just turning into my drive when another car came round the corner and drove into the back of mine.

W: Didn't you see him?

M: No, I didn't. I looked in my driving mirror and there was no one coming. Not only that, I also looked in the big mirror on the other side of the road.

W: So he must have been coming very fast if you didn't see him.

M: That's right. And he went straight into me.

Text 9

W: Good morning, Miss Smith's secretary.

M: Good morning, may I speak to Miss Smith, please?

W: I'm sorry. She's in conference at the moment. Do you want to leave a message?

M: Yes, all right. Can you tell her that Mr. Johnson called? And tell her that the meeting about the Trade Fair is on Thursday 12th at 2 pm.

W: Fine, is there anything else?

M: Yes. Could she phone to confirm that she can come before tomorrow?

W: Yes, and what number is it?

M: 802 9714 Extension 246.

W: Fine, I've got that. I'll get the message to her as soon as possible.

M: Thank you very much. Goodbye.

W: Goodbye.

Text 10

I flew to New York to take care of some business with Mr. Smith. But as soon as I arrived, I got sick, and could not meet with him. I had to call our appointment off. Then when I felt better I thought about visiting him at his home, but he lived too far away. I tried to telephone him during office hours, but he was busy. His secretary said that Mr. Smith would call me back, but he didn't. I gave up trying to make a new appointment because it would take more time and efforts than I wanted to spend.

A few days later, I saw a man on the street who looked like Mr. Smith, and I called out to him. It was someone else. When I returned to my hotel that day, I found a message which said that Mr. Smith had gone out of town on some sudden unexpected business. I was sorry that I had missed seeing him, but I was really enjoying my sightseeing in New York.

全真模拟卷(3)

M: Excuse me. Can you tell me how much the shirt is?

W: Yes, it's nine fifteen.

Text 1

W: I think I'll have the duck, please.

M: I'm very sorry, Madam. I'm afraid there isn't any left.

Text 2

W: Excuse me, visiting hours are over. It's time for you to leave.

M: I'm sorry, I didn't know the time or I would have left earlier.

Text 3

M: Are you going to London next weekend?

W: Yes, I will visit a friend of mine while I am there.

Text 4

M: I want a single room with a bath, what's the rate?

W: It's 25 a day. Your room number is 213. It is on the second floor. Here is your key.

Text 5

M: You'd better take your coat with you. It looks like it's going to snow.

W: You may be right. Thank you for mentioning this.

Text 6

M: We' re having a picnic tomorrow. Why don't you come with us?

W: I'd like to, but I think it's going to rain. The weatherman says so.

M: I don't think he is right. It hasn't rained for a week and it isn't cloudy, either.

W: But he is usually correct in his weather news.

M: The temperature is 32℃ this afternoon. I'm sure we'll have fine weather for our picnic.

W: Well, I'll go, but I'll take my umbrella with me.

Text 7

W: Excuse me, please. I seem to have lost my purse.

M: Oh, I see. Well, I'll have to fill out this lost and found report for you. It was a purse, you say?

W: That's right.

M: What is it like, ma'am?

W: Well, it's a black leather one with my driver's license, some name cards, and about fifty dollars in it.

M: Where did you last have it?

W: I'm pretty sure I had it when I was in the coffee shop.

M: When was that?

M: About 1:30 I think.

M: Where did you go after that?

W: To the shoe department, and then I came here.

M: I'm sure it will turn up. Now could you give me your name, address and phone number?

W: Mrs. Jane Thomas, 20 King Street, and my phone number is 89362124.

Text 8

M: Are you all right? You look off color.

W: I'm OK. I feel a bit tired. That's all.

M: That is because you work too hard, I suppose.

W: I guess so. Do you remember the new student in my class?

M: The boy from Haiti?

W: Yes, he is having a hard time communicating since he doesn't speak much English.

M: Do you have any other students from immigrant families in your class?

W: Oh, yes. This year we have a Korean, a Japanese, and a Chinese student. I spend a lot of time with them so that they can catch up.

M: I know. It's very kind of you to help them with their studies.

W: But it's really rewarding to see them make progress and fit well into the group.

M: That's true.

Text 9

W: I need to make some money so that I can take a trip to the north in February. Do you know any ways of making money?

M: How about delivering papers?

W: I already thought of that, but I don't have a bike.

M: How about walking dogs?

W: What? Walking dogs?

M: Yeah, you know, there are lots of people around here with little dogs. The dogs have to be walked every day. That's good for their health.

W: I don't know. How much can I make?

M: More than carrying papers.

W: Well, I do like animals. How do you go about finding dogs to walk?

M: Put an advertisement in the Sunday newspaper.

W: And how much is an ad?

M: An ad is under ten dollars, I'm sure. You can try for two dollars for half an hour—that would be ten dollars for five times a week. You can walk three or four dogs every day after school, you can get rich.

Text 10

A 60-year-old Australian woman jumped onto the back of a 4-metre crocodile to stop it from killing a 34-year-old man. The crocodile grabbed the man as he slept in a tent at a beach campsite in Australia. The crocodile entered the tent around 4 a. m. on Monday and dragged the man outside. The woman, who was camping nearby, saw what was happening and jumped onto the crocodile. The crocodile then let the man go and turned to the woman, pulling her towards the water, luckily a third person shot the crocodile dead just in time, saving the woman.

Text 11

Hello and welcome to the university library. This taped tour will introduce you to our library's facilities and operating hours. First of all, the library's collection of books, reference materials, and other resources are found on levels one to four of this building. Level one houses our humanities and map collections. On level two, you will find our circulation desk, current periodicals and journals, and our copy facilities. Our science and engineering sections can be found on level three. You can also find back issues of periodicals and journals older than six months on this level. Finally, group study rooms, our microfilm collection, and the multimedia center are located on level four.

Undergraduate students can check out up to ten books for two weeks. Graduate students can check out twenty books for four weeks. Books can be renewed up to two times. There is a 50-cent-a-day late fee for overdue books up to a maximum of $15. 00. Periodicals and reference books cannot be checked out.

The library is open weekdays, 8:00 a. m. to 10:00 p. m., and on Saturdays from 9 : 00 a. m. to 8 : 30 p. m. The library is closed on Sundays.

全真模拟卷(4)

M: Excuse me. Can you tell me how much the shirt is?

W: Yes, it's nine fifteen.

Text 1

W: Do you know anything about Agatha Christie?

M: Sure. She wrote many detective books.

Text 2

M: The lecture starts at 8:00.

W: Don't rush. We still have fifteen minutes to go.

Text 3

M: Listen! The show is starting.

W: How do you know?

M: Can't you hear the band? They are playing their instruments.

W: Sure, yes. Let's hurry up.

Text 4

W: How did you like the dinner just now?

M: It was quite delicious, but the beef was a bit well done.

Text 5

W: I'm free today. Can you think of doing something?

M: Well... How about taking a ride in the country?

W: Mmm. Good idea. We haven't taken it for ages.

Text 6

M: Aw, Jane! What did you have to go and do that for?

W: Do what?

M: You know what I am taking about. Why did you go and tell Mrs. Wallace how much money I am going to make? Now she will go and tell the whole world!

W: Well, I am sorry, Paul.

M: Yeah, but you know she talks to everybody and their brothers.

W: Well, I apologize. I guess I wasn't thinking. I got all excited.

M: Oh, well, it's done now. I guess it doesn't matter that much, anyway. They will know in the end. Everyone in this town got a big nose.

W: You know, it is really a lot of money for a first job...

Text 7

M: Susan, Please pass me a copy of *China Daily*.

W: Here you are.

M: I want to find what's on this weekend.

W: Is there anything good on?

M: The Beijing Opera is showing on Saturday evening. Do you like Beijing Opera?

W: Oh, yes. Very much. When and where will it be?

M: At 7:30 in Beihai Park.

W: Let's go and see it, OK?

M: Good idea!

Text 8

W: Where were you yesterday?

M: I was at home asleep.

W: Asleep! I thought that you had to take an exam.

M: I was sick. I had a fever. I couldn't get out of bed.

W: You still look a little sick. You must go back to bed.

M. I' m going now. I just came here to speak to my professor.

W: What did he tell you?

M: He said that I'd be able to take a make-up.

W: Well, that's all right then. Are you going straight home?

M: I have to stop at the drugstore on the way. I need some aspirin.

W: Do you think that you should walk that far?

M: I have to walk. I didn't bring my car. 1 didn't think I'd be able to drive today.

W: Well, take care of yourself.

M: OK. Thanks.

Text 9

W: What are you doing, Tom?

M: I' m writing to my mother.

W: But you wrote to her only yesterday.

M: Yes, but I have something new to tell her.

W: Something new?

M: Yes. I am telling her I've decided to take up a part-time job as a shop assistant.

W: What do you mean? You've been working at one nearly three months. Have you been fired by Rogers?

M: No. My mother doesn't know I have a part-time job.

W: You mean you didn't tell her before?

M: No. I didn't want her to worry about my study.

W: But why are you telling her now?

M. I don't want her to worry about my life here. You see, I told her that I'd just bought a car in my letter.

Text 10

Now, here is news:

An early morning fire damaged the Historic Geller House today. It destroyed the third floor of the building, but fire-fighters saved the first and the second floors. There were a few elderly people living in the building at the time and they were carried to safety. The Geller House was built in 1718, and was used as a hotel for over 150 years.

George Washington stayed here in 1782. The Geller's owned the house until 1930's. Then they sold it to Mill's family. Five years ago, it was made into a building for the elderly. Several fire departments were called to the scene. When we asked Fire Chief Andrew Barnes how the fire started, he answered that most likely a burning cigarette caused it. Chief Barnes promised a further investigation into the cause.

全真模拟卷(5)

M: Excuse me. Can you tell me how much the shirt is?

W: Yes, it's nine fifteen.

Text 1

W: Jimmy, take this umbrella with you.

M: Why? It's a fine day, isn't it?

W: Yes, but the weatherman said it' going to rain this afternoon.

Text 2

M: Here is a menu printed in English. What would you like, Judy?

W: Well, I think I'll have fried oysters first.

M: That's a good choice, since this is the season for oysters.

Text 3

M: My father does a lot of business and travels a lot. I like his job.

W: Are you going to study International Business at university, then?

M: I have not made up my mind yet, but very probably, yes.

Text 4

W: Tom.

M: Yes?

W: Will you please take this recorder to my office for me?

M: With pleasure. And let me carry some of the exercise books for you.

Text 5

W: I'll get someone to help you carry your luggage to your car.

M: If you don't mind, I'd like to have it delivered.

Text 6

M: How are you, Mrs. Brandon?

W: Pretty good. How are you doing?

M: Not so good. I lost my job today.

W: I'm sorry to hear that.

M: How are your students doing?

W: They are very nervous about their final test.

M: I remember you gave our class a hard final test in my first year of college. Many of us failed. But I really learned a lot from you. You see, I can speak very good English.

W: Thank you for saying so.

Text 7

M: Hello. This is Mike. Who is it, please?

W: Oh, Mike. This is Amy. My goodness! I've at last got hold of you.

M: Nice to hear from you again after all these years. What have you been doing?

W: Well, I've tried many things since school. I'm now working for a food processing company, in charge of sales. So I travel a lot.

M: Oh, that's great. You must really enjoy it.

W: Oh, I do. Yeah, it's interesting, but it's quite tiring. But, Hmm, what about you, Mike?

M: I work in a law firm, practicing in business law.

W: Oh, that's challenging.

M: Yeah, but I like my job.

Text 8

W: Good afternoon! Dr. Perkins' office.

M: Good afternoon. I'd like to speak to the doctor. Is he in?

W: Who is that calling, please?

M: My name is Li Hong. I'm from China.

W: I'm sorry. Dr. Perkins is now at an important meeting and can't answer your call.

M: I'm an exchange scholar. Dr. Perkins asked me to give a lecture. There are some details I want to discuss with him.

W: I see, but you must speak to himself about that. Oh, well, if you leave your number, I'll tell him to ring you as soon as he is available.

M: Thanks. My number is 7838298.

Text 9

W: Good morning. This is Shanghai Car Rental.

M: Good morning, Miss. A friend of mine suggested I call you to hire a car.

W: Oh, yes. A lot of people do this these days.

M: Yes, we are just on holiday here for a few days and they said it would be a good idea to hire a car to get around the city.

W: Well, it certainly is. What kind of car do you want to hire?

M: What can you suggest?

W: We have a variety of choice, such as Xiali, which is the cheapest, 200 yuan a day, Citroen, Jatta, Elysee, but Santana sedans are the big favorite these days.

M: How much if I hire a Santana for three days?

W: Oh, that will be 1,200 yuan.

M: On, it sounds a bit too expensive. What about a Jetta?

W: It will be 300 yuan a day.

M: Then I'd better hire a Jetta tomorrow morning. Would there be any problem?

W: No problem at all. Now let me take down your name and telephone number.

Text 10

W: Excuse me. I'm with the airport office. I'm doing a survey. Can I ask you some questions?

M: Sure. Go ahead.

W: How do you feel about the arrival area? Were you happy with it?

M: Yes, but it's a long way from the gate to the Immigration.

W: Oh, I'm sorry about that. Well, how about Immigration? How long did it take you to get through?

M: Oh, it's really quick—it took me only about 3 or 4 minutes.

W: Oh, good. OK, then, I see you bought some duty free items. Were you happy with the prices?

M: Well, I thought they were a little high.

W: A little high? Compared to?

M: Oh, to most places in Asia—although I will say the prices seem lower here than in the States.

W: I see. Well, how about the general appearance of the airport?

M: Oh, excellent. It's about the cleanest airport I've ever been in.

W: So, all in all it is clean and efficient?

M: Yes, oh, I've got to go, here comes my suitcase.

Text 11

This is radio station KSPF in Santa Monica, California. It's time for the noon weather report, brought to you today by the English Coffee Shop on Montana at Seventh Street in Santa Monica—open twenty-four hours a day with the best food in Santa Monica.

At twelve o'clock, the sun is out after a cloudy morning. The wind is from the west at three miles an hour, and the temperature is seventy-eight degrees with waves which are two to three feet high. Good waves! If you are driving to the beach this afternoon, park at the north end of the beach. The south end parking field is already full. Have a good time at the beach!

This weather report has been brought to you by the English Coffee Shop on Montana at Seventh Street in Santa Monica—open twenty-four hours a day with the best food in Santa Monica.

全真模拟卷(6)

M: Excuse me. Can you tell me how much the shirt is?

W: Yes, it's nine fifteen.

Text 1

M: Good morning, Mrs. Green. Come in, What can I do for you?

W: Well, I'm having difficulty sleeping. I often wake up at 3:00 in the morning and I just can't get back to sleep.

Text 2

M: It seems you are very busy recently, aren't you?

W: Yeah. I must work ten hours a day from Monday to Thursday, but on Friday I work only seven hours.

Text 3

M: Good evening, sir. Good evening, madam. There's a table for two over there. This way, please.

W: Thank you. Could we see the menu, please?

Text 4

M: I expect you could do with a cup of tea, couldn't you?

W: I'd rather have a cup of coffee, and a milky one without sugar, please.

Text 5

M: Have you done this before?

W: No. But if we follow the directions, we shouldn't have any trouble.

Text 6

M: Do you know Sam mo Hung, a Mr Rice Guy?

W: Of course. He is now 56 years old. And he started out studying aerobics, singing, dancing and kung fu at the age of nine, and has starred in 140 kung fu films. He has also become an independent producer and director.

M: You know only one aspect of him. Do you know what he could do in the kitchen?

W: I have no idea. Tell me.

M: In the kitchen, with his wife by his side he still puts on quite a dinnertime show.

W: What does he do there?

M: Imagine a big cook cutting vegetables on fast-forward. Picture a man making a fry, throwing the mixture up in the air, and then catching it, every last bit, in his frying pan. And his cooking motto is "Enjoy the moment." If you want to know how they cook, visit www. StudioClassroom. com. tw for the recipe.

Text 7

M: Well, my grandson is supposed to meet me in London at the airport. Do you think he'll be able to find me?

W: I'm sure he will. You don't have to worry about that. Are you going to be visiting him?

M: Yes. I've never seen my grandson.

W: I think you'll have a wonderful time in London. It's an attractive city. Is this your first time abroad?

M: No, I saw quite a bit of Europe before, Rome, Berlin, Paris, places like that, but I've never been to London.

W: Oh, then you have flown before, too.

M: No, that was during the Second World War and I went to Europe on a large warship.

W: Oh, things are quite different in Europe nowadays.

M: I'm sure they are. I'm really eager to get there.

W: Well, it's 4:00 pm now and we'll be there at 6:00 pm.

Text 8

M: Hello. I'm Peter. It looks like you had an accident.

W: Oh, yeah. Glad to meet you. I'm Linda. Right at the beginning of the skiing season.

M: That's too bad. Then, how did you break your arm?

W: Well, I guess you could say I fell off a mountain.

M: What happened?

W: I was in a ski-jumping competition. I landed the wrong way and fell the rest of the way down.

M: Wow! How far did you fall?

W: I'm not sure, but it was far enough to break my arm.

M: When can you ski again?

W: Probably in about two months. You know, I'm really mad at myself. Last year I broke my ankle in another ski-jumping competition.

M: Terrible! Why do you enter these contests, anyway?

W: Well, for the fun of it, of course. I like risk very much.

Text 9

W: My dear, it's five flights up!

M: That's all right. We'll get used to it. Besides, it is quiet up there. We're a little further away from the street and traffic noise and there's no one living over us.

W: Is the place well furnished?

M: Yes, it's pretty bright in there and big enough for our children to play.

W: What about the kitchen?

M: The stove and refrigerator are in good working order, and I don't see any loose electric wiring that could cause fires.

W: Are the pipes all right?

M: The pipelines seem OK, too. The toilet works well and the shower has hot and cold water and the sinks don't seem to leak.

W: The place is OK. Let's go there and have a look at it again.

M: OK, let's go.

Text 10

W: Thank you for coming to this meeting for students who will be remaining on campus during the ten-day winter break. As the Dean of Students, it is my responsibility to explain the vacation arrangements and to have you fill out forms giving the dates you will be on campus. To reduce heating costs, Butler Hall will be the only dormitory open. All the other dorms will close at 5 p. m., on Friday, Feb. 7th, and will not reopen until 6 p. m., on Feb. 16th. Once we have your completed forms, we will arrange you a room in Butler Hall. Please move all the belongings you will need to your vacation room by the 7th, as it will not be possible to reopen the other dorms during these ten days, once they have been closed. Most college facilities will be closed during the vacation. These facilities include the gymnasium, the college store, and the dining halls. The library and the computer center will be open, though on a reduced schedule. Only the post office and the college administration offices will be open on regular hours. Since I imagine most of you are staying here to finish up academic projects of one sort or another, let me wish you luck with your work. If you have any special problems, please do not hesitate to contact me at the Dean's

Office.

全真模拟卷(7)

M: Excuse me. Can you tell me how much the shirt is?

W: Yes, it's nine fifteen.

Text 1

W: If you want to get the car fixed in time, you'd better get a mechanic to do the job rather than do it all by yourself.

M: You have a point. But you know, to get a mechanic I'll have to make more money first.

Text 2

M: If you can make up your mind about the color, I can start on the outside of your house by early next week.

W: Well, right now I think I want white for the door and yellow for the wall, but I'll let you know tomorrow for sure.

Text 3

W: We're not going anywhere until you put on your seat belt!

M: All right! Take it easy! I' m just about to do it up.

W: Sorry. I didn't mean to jump on you. It's just that I get nervous when people don't wear seat belts.

Text 4

M: Is there any way I could get you to lend me your notes from Thursday's lecture? I have no idea where mine are, but I think you were in the class, right?

W: Well, yeah, I did take notes. But actually they're now with another friend.

M: Oh, it's a pity.

Text 5

W: I wish you wouldn't have your TV so loud.

M: Sorry! Are you trying to sleep?

W: Yes, and while I think of it—please ask when you borrow the iron.

M: I really ought to have known better. Sorry!

Text 6

W: Do you have any suggestions for getting along with others? It seems that none of my classmates likes me.

M: Is that so serious? Don't be so pessimistic; at least you have my friendship.

W: Well, except you.

M: I heard that you and Lucy had a quarrel yesterday.

W: You mean that spoiled rich kid?

M: Actually she is kind-hearted, too. Could you tell me why you quarreled?

W: Just for a small thing. Well, I thought she was just a rich princess, but it seems that we have a lot in common.

M: I'm glad you've realized that at last. You don't really hate each other, so why don't you make up?

W: You mean I take the initiative? No, that's the last thing I want to do.

M: Come on, you can do it.

W: Well, not now, maybe later.

M: OK. It doesn't matter as long as you do it.

W: Thank you. You helped a lot.

Text 7

W: Hi. I'm looking to rent a car for a week.

M: Are you at least 25 with valid driver's license and a valid credit card?

W: Yes. And yes.

M: What model were you thinking about?

W: What's your economy model?

M: The Hyundai Accent. It's $135.99 per week plus taxes. All cars come with unlimited mileage.

W: Not bad. What's your high-end car?

M: A Ford Mustang. It would suit you two ladies very well!

W: Hmm. How much with tax?

M: The base price for one week is $288.95, plus two dollars per day for the license fee, and local taxes. The total is $327.94.

Text 8

M: What seems to be the trouble, Ms. Lee?

W: I have a terrible pain in my stomach.

M: I see. How long has this pain been occurring?

W: Since late last night.

M: I see. Let me have a look, shall I? What did you eat yesterday?

W: We went to an American seafood restaurant, and then we went to eat Chinese food. After that, we had a lot of Italian things such as ...

M: Did you throw up, or did you have the runs?

W: Both.

M: Well, that could be an upset stomach from overeating. Allergic to any drugs?

W: No.

M: All right. Take the medicine every six hours and stay in bed today.

W: Thank you, doctor.

Text 9

M: Cathy, playing tennis seems very interesting.

W: Would you like to learn?

M: Yes. How do you play?

W: Tennis can be played in singles or doubles. The outside lines are for double, and the inside lines are for singles.

M: How do you decide who starts serving?

W: Well, you can use a coin toss to decide. Whoever wins chooses either to serve or the side of the court.

M: How do you count the score?

W: At the beginning, the score would be LOVE LOVE.

M: Love means "0"?

W: You got it. It then counts to 15, 30, and 40. If you get to 40 and win again, you win the game.

M: The opponent starts serving then?

W: Right. See. You know how to play now.

M: Let's try it sometime.

W: Sure!

Text 10

W: The sense of hearing is one of our most important means of knowing what is going on around us. We are warned of danger by sound. Sounds serve to please us in music. It has a waste product, too, in the form of noise. Noise has been called unwanted sound. Noise is growing and it may get much worse before it gets any better.

Automobiles, trucks, buses, motorcycles, airplanes, boats, factories, bands—all these things make noise. They bother not only our ears but our minds and bodies as well.

There is a saying about it being so noisy that you can't hear yourself think. Doctors who study noise believe that we must sometimes hear ourselves think. If we don't, we may have headaches, other aches and pains, or even worse mental problems. Noise adds stress to our society that already faces enough.

There are two ways to cut down on the harm caused by noise. One is to cut down on the amount of noise. The other is to protect ourselves against the noise we can't stop.

Ways of making less noise are now being tested. There are groups for the prevention of noise in this country. There is even a law controlling noise. We cannot return to the "good old days" of peace and quiet. But we can reduce noise—if we shout loudly enough about it.

全真模拟卷(8)

M: Excuse me. Can you tell me how much the shirt is?

W: Yes, it's nine fifteen.

Text 1

M: Type and copy this contract before Friday.

W: How many copies do you want?

M: Twenty.

Text 2

M: Good morning. I'd like to apply for a bankcard.

W: OK. Please show me your ID card and fill in this form.

Text 3

W: Will it be all right if I meet you at ten?

M: I'm sorry I won't be free then. Let's make it an hour later.

Text 4

W: What's the matter?

M: I'm not feeling so well.

W: Get some rest and take these three times a day. If you don't feel better in a week, come back and see me.

Text 5

W: Are you interested in sports?

M: Yeah, I like sports a lot, especially basketball. I play with a group of guys every Saturday at the park.

W: Oh, really? But I think basketball is the most boring game in the world! Have you ever played soccer? It's much more exciting than basketball. Although I'm not good at it, I go and watch a game at least twice a month.

Text 6

W: Good morning, Mr. Sharp. I'm very sorry I'm late.

M: You're late every morning, Miss Smith. You were late Tuesday; yesterday... Don't you have a watch?

W: Yes. But it wasn't my fault. I stood in the rain for an hour this morning. I waited and waited for a bus, and

then when one came, it was full.

M: How about yesterday and the day before yesterday?

W: Well, I came by taxi yesterday and...

M: And you were still late! And Tuesday?

W: Tuesday I went to see the doctor and I sat in his chair for about two hours. It was terrible...

M: I see. And tomorrow, Miss Smith?

Text 7

W: I understand how you feel, sir. But there simply isn't any table. The person who was in charge of your booking must have forgotten to write it down. I'm afraid it was just a mistake. He is new here, you see.

M: Just a mistake? Do you realize I've invited some important people for dinner? That mistake could make me lose an important business partner.

W: I'm sorry, sir. I suggest you call them and explain the problem. I'm sure you will find several other good restaurants around here.

M: I can't get in touch with them now. They are probably on their way at this very moment. Surely you could fit one more table in.

W: Not unless you'd like me to put yours in the hall, sir.

M: Well, OK. That's better than nothing.

Text 8

M: Hi, Alice, have you made any New Year's wishes?

W: Just the usual. I'd like to lose some weight, and I want to save some money.

M: Come on! Everybody makes such wishes.

W: I know, Henry. Well, I hope I'll get a good job after I graduate this summer, but that's not a resolution. I'm going to work harder. How about you?

M: Hmm, I stopped smoking last June. That was last year's promise to myself.

W: So what do you want to do this year?

M: I want to start getting more exercises. I have to lose weight, so I'd like to join a health club.

W: I'd like to, too. Jeff told me he'd like to have a really nice vacation.

M: Oh? Where did he think he would go?

W: He might go to a quiet beach in Mexico, or go fishing in Canada. He hasn't made up his mind yet.

Text 9

W: Alan, I heard that you went to the clinic today. What's the matter?

M: I burnt my arm and hurt my head.

W: What happened?

M: This morning, I wanted to have some noodles, so I boiled some hot water. I was pouring the hot water into the cup when my cat suddenly jumped onto the table and knocked it all over my arm. It really hurt so I decided to go and see the doctor.

W: How did you hurt your head then?

M: As I was walking to the doctor's, I passed some workers painting our building. A can of paint fell off one of their ladders right in front of me. I tried to get out of the way and hit my head against a window.

W: What a terrible morning!

M: Yes, but I finally made it to the clinic. The doctor told me to keep my arm clean and dry and to rest today. I'm feeling better now.

Text 10

John first entered high school four years ago, at the age of 16. He worked very hard and always got very good grades. Besides doing well in his lessons, he was very active in sports, getting up every morning to practice running; he never took the bus to school but always ran instead. He even won a silver medal in the 800-meter race at the school sports meeting a year ago. As a reward, his parents bought him something that he had wanted to have for a long time—a computer.

Soon, things began to change. He stopped getting up early and never ran to school. His interest in sports suddenly disappeared. Sometimes he got up so late that he would miss the school bus and then miss school.

Soon his school work began to suffer. One night, quite late, John's mother saw light on in his room. She went in and found John still awake, playing computer games. Finally the reason for John's change was clear—ever since he had been given the computer, he had been staying up late every night to play games. His lack of sleep was having a terrible effect on his studies. His mom decided that this must be stopped. The next day she had a serious talk with John. Instead of taking away his computer, she told him he was old enough to learn how to control himself.

John had already begun to realize how serious the problem was, so when his mother spoke to him, he agreed to work on controlling himself. He was rather glad to know that his mother cared about him so much.

全真模拟卷(9)

M: Excuse me. Can you tell me how much the shirt is?

W: Yes, it's nine fifteen.

Text 1

W: Hi, David! Nice to meet you here in the library!

M: Me too. Do you know where Linda is?

W: I'm just going to meet her in my office in half an hour. She's now having her class.

Text 2

M: How about driving into the country on Thursday?

W: Well, I'll see if I can get the afternoon off, and I'd like to see my parents first.

Text 3

W: How was your research going, Jack?

M: Well, not bad. I talked to some students and got their opinions. And now I've got to write the paper based on the information I've collected.

Text 4

W: Tom said he could get your club some tickets to the game if you're interested.

M: If we are interested. Look, Susan. We've been trying to get tickets everywhere.

Text 5

M: It's sunny and warm. Stop studying and come into the garden with me.

W: Why not?

Text 6

M: Is everything going well according to the plan?

W: Our store will open two weeks before Christmas.

M: I guess we should announce ourselves soon. Tell people we're coming. Put up a big sign.

W: Sure. The minute they see the sign, they will be lining up.

M: To show their anger.

W: Yeah. They are lining up not to buy things but to show their anger. Because some people think chain

stores all look the same.

M: They'll hate us in the beginning. But we'll satisfy them in the end.

Text 7

W: Can't you do something about the service in the hotel, manager?

M: I'm sorry madam. What's the problem exactly?

W: My breakfast, that's the problem.

M: Yes?

W: I ordered breakfast from room service. Oh, at least half an hour ago.

M: Yes?

W: I've telephoned room service three times, but my breakfast still hasn't come.

M: I see.

W: I've got an important meeting at nine o'clock. An now it seems I'll have to go there without breakfast. Really, I don't think this is good enough.

M: I'm very sorry about this madam. You ordered breakfast half an hour ago and you've phoned three times since then.

W: That's right.

M: I'm really sorry about that. You should have received your breakfast no later than five to ten minutes after you had ordered it.

W: That's what I thought.

M: The problem may be that there are short of people in the kitchens recently. But I'll look into this. And I'll make sure that the breakfast is sent to you immediately. Full English breakfast, was it?

W: Yes. Full English breakfast.

M: Very well madam. I'll deal with this myself and I'll have it sent up to your room right away.

Text 8

M: Morrie, what is an AHT?

W: Well, AHT stands for animal health technician. I graduated from California's first AHT class at Peals College. Some of us may work in the countryside taking care of cattle horses or sheep. Some may work in research labs. But most of us work in pet hospitals.

M: I know that you work in a pet hospital. What do you do there?

W: We run blood and other tests, give shorts and prepare medicine. We also cut nails, clean teeth, give bathe and clean the cages. We help keep the clinic running smoothly, making sure there is enough of medicine and equipment.

M: Indeed, you have so much to do. Doctor Blake told me that he couldn't have done so much without you.

Text 9

M: Where are you going on vacation this year?

W: Well, we were thinking about going on the voyage to the Caribbean Sea. It's a beautiful part of the world.

M: It certainly is. I went on one last year. But the weather can sometimes be really bad.

W: I know. I have been reading weather reports for the Caibbean on the Internet. They seem to have lots of storms.

M: They certainly do. When we went on a voyage we stopped at Jomaker. And the islands had been hit by storms two weeks before. You could still see a lot of damage.

W: Well, if I decide to go, I'll just have to hope for the best.

Text 10

Well I'd love to share with you something about my life. I was a director of labor relations for a big company ten years ago. And I should have been happy. I had everything that I thought I wanted. But going into work everyday took away a bit of myself. Until finally I stopped and said, "Where is that lively college girl who used to read tens of books and do fun things? Where is she?" I knew I have to look for her. Then one day, walking through a children's bookstore, it hit me. I loved these books. The richness of the pictures, the power of these words. I gathered an armful of books and said, "This is what I want to do." And since then, I have treated writing like a full time job. I wrote over twenty stories in the next year. And most of them got sent back with letters saying they were not good enough. But I didn't give up. I think it's because of that love that I have been able not to just write one book but nine books in the last ten years. When I worked in the company, I worked sixty-hour weeks because I had to. Now I work sixty-hour weeks because I love it. If I hadn't made that choice to take a chance to do something that really thrilled me, I don't think I could have lived with myself.

全真模拟卷(10)

M: Excuse me. Can you tell me how much the shirt is?

W: Yes, it's nine fifteen.

Text 1

W: And so ... I think we need to ...

M: Excuse me, Miss Louis, I hate to interrupt, but I think we should slow down the production and pay more attention to quality.

Text 2

M: Do you think I am going too fast?

W: Of course, the speed limit here is 55 miles per hour, and you are going 15 miles over it.

Text 3

W: So, what do think? Do they suit me?

M: Well, they are nice jackets, but they make you look fat.

W: OK, I will leave them then.

Text 4

M: Well, now, before we order, let's agree first that we each pay our own bill.

W: OK, I agree.

M: And, what do you say, Barbara and Charles?

Text 5

W: Can we have chicken for dinner?

M: I don't see why not.

W: Great, how do we like it cooked?

M: It doesn't matter.

Text 6

W: So here is your key, Mr. McDonald. The luggage will be brought to your room.

M: Thanks, I will need a meeting room tomorrow. Do you have one in the hotel?

W: Yes, we do. You can ask our hotel manager in the morning.

M: One more thing. Is the restaurant still open?

W: I'm afraid not.

M: Never mind. I will call room service. Thanks for your help.

Text 7

W: How can I help you, sir?

M: Could you break a 20 for me?

W: Sure. How do you want it?

M: Could I have two fives and the rest in ones.

W: Well, I have some fives but I don't have enough ones. Are quarters OK with you?

M: OK, that's even better. In that case, I won't have to worry about the small change for photocopying. I need to prepare a lot of materials for my study.

W: Here you go.

M: Thanks a million.

Text 8

M: At just twenty-three, Betty, the pop star has a handful of records to her name. Now she will talk to me about herself. Where do you come from?

W: I grew up in west London. And I was actually born there as well. My mom is from Scotland and my father is from Singapore. He came over when he was 17 or something to England and met my mom and they got married.

M: So have you ever been to Singapore?

W: Actually it's funny. You should say that, because I went to Singapore for my holiday this year. I did the whole tourist thing and I really enjoyed it. It was quite nice seeing people that looked like my dad. I really loved it and the people were lovely. There are Chinese, Indians, and English. So there are three different kinds of customs there. You can walk to one part of the town, and it's like India; and in another part, it's like Europe; and in another part, it's like China. So you see, in one country, you can experience different customs from three different societies. That is something special about Singapore. And I also think Singapore has got the best food.

M: Did you get looked at a lot over there?

W: Yeah, I did, because people thought I was half something, and they liked my skin, so I got quite a lot of people looking at me, which was quite annoying.

Text 9

W: Did you report a break in to us just now?

M: Well, it isn't my place. I am just staying here for two months while my friends are out of the city. So besides the TV set and some paintings, I don't really know what else is missing. All the drawers had been emptied out and I guess some things were taken. My friends will be mad.

W: I see. Now ...

M: It wasn't my fault, of course. All the windows and doors were locked.

W: Now how exactly did you discover the break in?

M: I went out at 7 o'clock as I do every Thursday to attend my computer class. Afterwards I stopped at a café for a drink and I got back here just after 11 o'clock.

W: How can you be so sure of the time?

M: Because I was at the café till the ten o'clock news was over, and it's only a two-minute walk from here. Is there any chance of anything being recovered? I know my friends will be especially sad about the paintings.

W: We'll do our best and let you know if we find anything. And if I were you, I would immediately call my friends.

Text 10

Don't you think the world would be an easier place to live in, if we all spoke the same language? There are thousands of different languages spoken around the globe, so it's no wonder we have such difficulties understanding one another. If you are going to choose a language, which everyone in the world would learn, which would you choose? Chinese is spoken by more people than any other language, and English has already been selected as the international language of business and science. Many other people have tried to find an answer to this problem. One of them was Dr. Zamenhof—a Polish word expert. In 1887, he introduced Esperanto—a totally new language to the world. Thousands of people took it seriously and began to learn to speak it. Today Esperanto is still spoken by eight million people around the world, and it is a language accepted by the Post Office, so if you address some letter in Esperanto, it will get to the correct place.